Teacher Reference Handbook

Macmillan McGraw-Hill

Math Connects

5

BIGHORN MOUNTAIN

BLACK DIAMOND SLOPE
GREEN CIRCLE SLOPE

Macmillan/McGraw-Hill

**Macmillan
McGraw-Hill**

The *McGraw·Hill* Companies

Send all inquiries to:
Macmillan/McGraw-Hill
8787 Orion Place
Columbus, OH 43240-4027

ISBN-13: 978-0-02-107526-3
MHID: 0-02-107526-3

Grade 5 Teacher Reference Handbook

Printed in the United States of America.

1 2 3 4 5 6 7 8 9 10 079 15 14 13 12 11 10 09 08 07 06

Teacher Reference Handbook

Contents

Scope and Sequence

Number and Operations	PreK	Kindergarten	Grade 1	Grade 2	Grade 3	Grade 4	Grade 5	Course 1	Course 2	Course 3	Pre-Algebra	Algebra 1	Geometry
Whole Numbers													
One-to-one correspondence	●	●	●	●	●	●	●						
Count, read, write, name, rename, represent Numbers to 10	●	●	●	●	●	●	●						
Numbers to 30		●	●	●	●	●	●						
Numbers to 100			●	●	●	●	●						
Numbers to 1,000				●	●	●	●						
Numbers to 10,000					●	●	●						
Numbers to 1 million						●	●						
Numbers to billions							●						
Skip count			●	●	●	●	●						
Equivalent Forms (word, expanded, standard)	●	●	●	●	●	●	●	●					
Place value		●	●	●	●	●	●	●	●				
Powers and exponents							●	●	●	●	●	●	●
Negative-integer exponents										●	●	●	
Scientific notation										●	●		
Round whole numbers			●	●	●	●	●	●					
Compare and order whole numbers		●	●	●	●	●	●	●					
Represent on a number line		●	●	●	●	●	●						
Even and odd numbers, doubles			●	●	●	●							
Factors and multiples					●	●	●	●	●	●	●	●	
Prime and composite numbers						●	●	●	●	●	●	●	
Prime factorization						●	●	●	●	●	●		

 Introduce   Develop   Reinforce   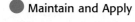 Maintain and Apply   Prerequisite Skills

	PreK	Kindergarten	Grade 1	Grade 2	Grade 3	Grade 4	Grade 5	Course 1	Course 2	Course 3	Pre-Algebra	Algebra 1	Geometry
Greatest common factor (GCF)						◐	●	●	●	●	●	●	
Least common multiple (LCM)							●	●	●	●	●	●	
Perfect squares, cubes, roots								◐	●	●	●	●	●

Fractions

	PreK	Kindergarten	Grade 1	Grade 2	Grade 3	Grade 4	Grade 5	Course 1	Course 2	Course 3	Pre-Algebra	Algebra 1	Geometry
Model fractional parts of a whole, of a set or group	○	○	◐	●	●	●	●	●	●	●			
Read and write fractions			○	◐	●	●	●	●	●	●	●	●	●
Represent fractions on a number line				◐	◐	●	●	●	●	●	●	●	●
Compare and order fractions				◐	◐	◐	●	●	●	●	●	●	●
Equivalent fractions					◐	◐	●	●	●	●	●	●	●
Simplify fractions					○	◐	◐	●	●	●	●	●	●
Least common denominator (LCD)							◐	●	●	●	●	●	●
Reciprocal, multiplicative inverse								◐	●	●	●	●	●
Mixed numbers and improper fractions						◐	●	●	●	●	●	●	●
Relate fractions and decimals					○	◐	●	●	●	●	●	●	●

Decimals

	PreK	Kindergarten	Grade 1	Grade 2	Grade 3	Grade 4	Grade 5	Course 1	Course 2	Course 3	Pre-Algebra	Algebra 1	Geometry
Model decimals					○	◐	●	●	●	●	●	●	●
Read and write decimals					◐	●	●	●	●	●	●	●	●
Represent decimals on a number line						◐	●	●	●	●	●	●	●
Compare and order decimals						◐	●	●	●	●	●	●	●
Round decimals						◐	●	●	●	●	●	●	●
Terminating and repeating decimals								◐	●	●	●	●	●
Non-repeating decimals/ irrational numbers												◐	●

Scope and Sequence

Number and Operations

Ratio, Rate, Proportion	PreK	Kindergarten	Grade 1	Grade 2	Grade 3	Grade 4	Grade 5	Course 1	Course 2	Course 3	Pre-Algebra	Algebra 1	Geometry
Concept of a ratio							●	●	●	●	●	●	●
Model ratios							●	●	●	●	●	●	●
Read and write ratios							●	●	●	●	●	●	●
Relate ratios to fractions							●	●	●	●	●	●	●
Rates							●	●	●	●	●	●	●
Unit rate							●	●	●	●	●	●	●
Rate of change								●	●	●	●	●	●
Direct variation								●	●	●	●	●	
Ratio and probability								●	●	●	●	●	
Solve proportions							●	●	●	●	●	●	●
Proportional reasoning								●	●	●	●	●	●
Scale drawings								●	●	●	●	●	
Scale factor								●	●	●	●	●	
Similar figures								●	●	●	●	●	●
Indirect measurement								●	●	●	●	●	
Dilations											●		●

Percent	PreK	Kindergarten	Grade 1	Grade 2	Grade 3	Grade 4	Grade 5	Course 1	Course 2	Course 3	Pre-Algebra	Algebra 1	Geometry
Concept of percent, model								●	●	●	●	●	
Relate fractions and decimals to percents								●	●	●	●	●	
Percent of a number								●	●	●	●	●	
Percent one number is of another									●	●	●	●	
Percent proportion $(\frac{P}{B} = \frac{R}{100})$									●	●	●	●	

● Introduce   ● Develop   ● Reinforce   ● Maintain and Apply   ● Prerequisite Skills

	PreK	Kindergarten	Grade 1	Grade 2	Grade 3	Grade 4	Grade 5	Course 1	Course 2	Course 3	Pre-Algebra	Algebra 1	Geometry
Percent equation ($RB = P$)								◐	●	●	●		
Percent of change								◐	●	●	●		
Interest, profit, discount								◐	●	●	●		

Integers

	PreK	Kindergarten	Grade 1	Grade 2	Grade 3	Grade 4	Grade 5	Course 1	Course 2	Course 3	Pre-Algebra	Algebra 1	Geometry
Concept of integers, negative numbers							○	●	●	●	●	●	●
Read and write integers							○	●	●	●	●	●	●
Represent on a number line							○	●	●	●	●	●	●
Compare and order integers							○	●	●	●	●	●	●
Absolute value								◐	●	●	●	●	●

Rational Numbers

	PreK	Kindergarten	Grade 1	Grade 2	Grade 3	Grade 4	Grade 5	Course 1	Course 2	Course 3	Pre-Algebra	Algebra 1	Geometry
Identify and simplify rational numbers								◐	●	●	●	●	
Represent on a number line								◐	●	●	●	●	
Relate rational numbers to decimals								◐	●	●	●	●	
Compare and order rational numbers								◐	●	●	●	●	●

Real Numbers

	PreK	Kindergarten	Grade 1	Grade 2	Grade 3	Grade 4	Grade 5	Course 1	Course 2	Course 3	Pre-Algebra	Algebra 1	Geometry
Identify irrational numbers								◐	●	●	●	●	
Represent irrational, real numbers on a number line								◐	●	●	●	●	
Identify and classify real numbers								○	●	●	●	●	
Estimate square roots								◐	●	●	●	●	

Scope and Sequence

Number and Operations

	PreK	Kindergarten	Grade 1	Grade 2	Grade 3	Grade 4	Grade 5	Course 1	Course 2	Course 3	Pre-Algebra	Algebra 1	Geometry
Understand Operations													
Model, meaning of addition	●	●	◐	●	●	●	●						
Model, meaning of subtraction	●	●	◐	●	●	●	●						
Meaning of multiplication: repeated addition, equal groups, arrays				◐	◐	●	●						
Meaning of division: equal groups, repeated subtraction				●	◐	●	●						
Inverse operations: relate addition and subtraction; multiplication and division			●	◐	◐	●	●						
Check subtraction by adding				◐	●	●	●						
Operations: Whole Numbers													
Add whole numbers — Basic facts	●	●	◐	●	●	●	●	●	●	●			
Fact families		●	◐	●	●	●	●	●	●	●			
Count on, doubles			●	●	●	●	●						
Number line			●	●	●	●	●	●	●	●			
Algorithm (regroup), partial sums			●	◐	●	●	●	●	●	●			
Three or more addends				◐	●	●	●	●	●	●			
Subtract whole numbers — Basic facts	●	●	◐	●	●	●	●	●	●	●			
Fact families			◐	●	●	●	●	●	●	●			
Count back			◐	●	●	●	●	●	●	●			
Number line			◐	●	●	●	●	●	●	●			
Algorithm (regroup)			●	◐	●	●	●	●	●	●			

● Introduce   ● Develop   ● Reinforce   ● Maintain and Apply   ● Prerequisite Skills

	PreK	Kindergarten	Grade 1	Grade 2	Grade 3	Grade 4	Grade 5	Course 1	Course 2	Course 3	Pre-Algebra	Algebra 1	Geometry
Multiply whole numbers Basic facts				◐	●	●	●	●	●				
Fact families, related facts				◐	●	●	●	●	●				
Multiply three numbers					◐	●	●	●	●				
Algorithm (regroup)				◐	●	●	●	●	●				
Divide whole numbers Basic facts				◐	●	●	●	●	●				
Fact families, related facts				◐	●	●	●	●	●				
Algorithm					◐	●	●	●	●				
Remainders					◐	●	●	●	●				

Operations: Fractions

	PreK	Kindergarten	Grade 1	Grade 2	Grade 3	Grade 4	Grade 5	Course 1	Course 2	Course 3	Pre-Algebra	Algebra 1	Geometry
Add and subtract fractions and mixed numbers Like denominators							◐	●	●	●	●	●	
Unlike denominators							◐	●	●	●	●	●	
Multiply and divide fractions, mixed numbers								●	●	●	●	●	

Operations: Decimals

	PreK	Kindergarten	Grade 1	Grade 2	Grade 3	Grade 4	Grade 5	Course 1	Course 2	Course 3	Pre-Algebra	Algebra 1	Geometry
Add and subtract decimals Money amounts				○	●	●	●						
Non-money amounts					◐	●	●	●	●	●	●		
Multiply decimals						○	●	●	●	●	●		
Divide decimals						○	●	●	●	●	●		

Operations: Integers, Rational, Real Numbers

	PreK	Kindergarten	Grade 1	Grade 2	Grade 3	Grade 4	Grade 5	Course 1	Course 2	Course 3	Pre-Algebra	Algebra 1	Geometry
Add and subtract integers								◐	●	●	●	●	●
Multiply and divide integers								◐	●	●	●	●	●

Number and Operations	PreK	Kindergarten	Grade 1	Grade 2	Grade 3	Grade 4	Grade 5	Course 1	Course 2	Course 3	Pre-Algebra	Algebra 1	Geometry
Rules of exponents								◐	●	●	●	●	●
Add, subtract, multiply, and divide rational numbers									◐	●	●	●	●
Add, subtract, multiply, and divide real numbers												◐	●

Mental Arithmetic and Estimation Strategies	PreK	Kindergarten	Grade 1	Grade 2	Grade 3	Grade 4	Grade 5	Course 1	Course 2	Course 3	Pre-Algebra	Algebra 1	Geometry
Add and subtract multiples of powers of 10			○	●	●	●	●	●	●				
Multiply multiples of powers of 10				◐	◐	●	●	●	●				
Divide multiples of powers of 10					◐	●	●	●	●				
Use addition properties						◐	●	●	●				
Use compensation						◐	●	●	●				
Estimation	◐	◐	●	●	●	●	●	●	●				
Rounding			○	◐	●	●	●	●	●				
Estimate sums			○	◐	●	●	●	●	●	●			
Estimate differences			○	◐	●	●	●	●	●	●			
Estimate products				◐	◐	●	●	●	●	●			
Estimate quotients					◐	●	●	●	●	●			
Use compatible numbers, clustering				○	◐	●	●	◐					
Estimate with fractions									◐	●	●		
Estimate percents								◐	●	●	●		
Estimate square roots									◐	●	●	●	●

○ Introduce   ● Develop   ● Reinforce   ● Maintain and Apply   ● Prerequisite Skills

Algebra

Use Patterns

	PreK	Kindergarten	Grade 1	Grade 2	Grade 3	Grade 4	Grade 5	Course 1	Course 2	Course 3	Pre-Algebra	Algebra 1	Geometry
Sort and classify by attribute	○	◐	●	●	●								
Identify, describe patterns	○	○	◐	●	●	●	●						
Extend patterns	○	◐	●	●	●	●	●						
Create patterns	○	○	◐	●	●	●	●						
Number patterns			◐	●	●	●	●						
Use addition and subtraction patterns				◐	●	●	●						
Use multiplication patterns					◐	●	●						
Use division patterns							◐						

Properties

	PreK	Kindergarten	Grade 1	Grade 2	Grade 3	Grade 4	Grade 5	Course 1	Course 2	Course 3	Pre-Algebra	Algebra 1	Geometry
Associative and Commutative Properties			○	●	●	●	○	●	●	●	●	●	
Identity Properties			○	◐	●	●	○	●	●	●	●	●	
Zero Property of Multiplication				◐	●	●	●	●	●	●	●	●	
Distributive Property					◐	●	●	●	●	●	●	●	
Order of operations					◐	●	●	●	●	●	●	●	
Addition and Subtraction Properties of Equality							◐	●	●	●	●	●	
Multiplication and Division Properties of Equality							○	●	●	●	●	●	
Additive Inverse Property							○	●	●	●	●	○	
Multiplicative Inverse Property								◐	●	●	●	●	
Closure Property												◐	●
Properties of equalities and inequalities												◐	●

Scope and Sequence

Algebra

Algebraic Representations

	PreK	Kindergarten	Grade 1	Grade 2	Grade 3	Grade 4	Grade 5	Course 1	Course 2	Course 3	Pre-Algebra	Algebra 1	Geometry
Write and solve number sentences using symbols, +, -, =		●	◐	●	●	●	●						
Missing addends or factors			◐	●	●	●	●						
Variables, expressions, equations					●	◐	●	●	●	●	●	●	●
Order of operations						◐	●	●	●	●	●	●	●
Evaluate algebraic expressions						◐	●	●	●	●	●	●	●
Write algebraic expressions and equations					●	◐	●	●	●	●	●	●	●
Use formulas						●	●	●	●	●	●	●	●
Inequalities with variables									◐	●	●	●	
Equivalent expressions; simplify expressions								◐	●	◐	●	●	●
Monomials									◐	●	●	●	●
Operations with monomials									◐	●	●	●	●
Polynomials, definition										◐	●	●	●
Operations with polynomials										◐	●	●	●
Factor polynomials												◐	●
Pythagorean Theorem								◐	●	●	●	●	●
Distance formula										◐	●	●	●
Radical expressions												◐	●
Rational expressions, algebraic fractions											◐	◐	●

● Introduce   ● Develop   ● Reinforce   ● Maintain and Apply   ● Prerequisite Skills

Solve Equations and Inequalities

	PreK	Kindergarten	Grade 1	Grade 2	Grade 3	Grade 4	Grade 5	Course 1	Course 2	Course 3	Pre-Algebra	Algebra 1	Geometry
Addition and subtraction equations					○	◐	●	●	●	●	●	●	
Multiplication and division equations						◐	●	●	●	●	●	●	
Multiple-step equations								◐	●	●	●	●	
Equations with variables on both sides									◐	●	●	●	
Solve inequalities								○	◐		●	●	
Graph inequalities									◐	●	●	●	●
Multiple-step inequalities											◐	●	●
Compound inequalities												◐	●
Absolute-value equations, inequalities												◐	
Quadratic equations, graphing and factoring												◐	

Graph Linear and Nonlinear Equations and Inequalities

	PreK	Kindergarten	Grade 1	Grade 2	Grade 3	Grade 4	Grade 5	Course 1	Course 2	Course 3	Pre-Algebra	Algebra 1	Geometry
Relationships between equations and their graphs						○	○	◐	●	●	●	●	●
Linear equations								◐	●	●	●	●	●
Rate of change								◐	◐	●	●	●	●
Slope								◐	●	●	●	●	●
Intercepts								◐	●	●	●	●	●
Slope-intercept form									◐	◐	●	●	●
Point-slope form										○	◐	●	●
Systems of linear equations and inequalities, graph and solve									◐	◐	◐	●	●

Scope and Sequence

Algebra	PreK	Kindergarten	Grade 1	Grade 2	Grade 3	Grade 4	Grade 5	Course 1	Course 2	Course 3	Pre-Algebra	Algebra 1	Geometry
Functions and Relations													
Function tables				◐	◐	●	●	●	●	●	●	●	
Function rules				◐	◐	●	●	●	●	●	●	●	
Definition of function				●	●	●	◐	◐	◐	●	●	●	
Definition of relation, mapping											◐		
Domain and range of functions									●	◐	●	●	
f(x) notation										◐		◐	
Vertical-line test for functions											◐	●	
Identify linear and nonlinear functions, relationships									◐	◐	●	●	
Graph ordered pairs					●	◐	●	●	◐	●	◐		
Graph functions						◐			◐	●	●	◐	
Graph relationships								◐	●	●	●	●	
Model real-world data						◐	◐	●	●	●	●	●	
Proportional relationships, direct variation								◐	●	●	●	●	
Inverse variation									●		◐	●	
Quadratic functions										◐	◐	●	
Exponential functions											●	◐	
Rational functions												◐	
Absolute-value functions												◐	
Families of linear functions										●	◐	●	
Families of nonlinear functions										●	◐	●	
Arithmetic sequences								◐	●	◐	●	◐	

● Introduce ● Develop ● Reinforce ◐ Maintain and Apply ◐ Prerequisite Skills

Measurement

Length, Weight, Mass, Area, Capacity, Volume	PreK	Kindergarten	Grade 1	Grade 2	Grade 3	Grade 4	Grade 5	Course 1	Course 2	Course 3	Pre-Algebra	Algebra 1	Geometry
Compare and order	○	○	◐	●	●	●	●						
Nonstandard units	○	○	◐	●	●								
Customary units			○	◐	●	●	●	◐	●	●	●	●	●
Metric units				◐	●	●	●	●	●	●	●	●	●
Estimate measurements				◐	●	●	●						
Convert units within a system				○	○	●	●	●	●	●	●	●	●

Temperature	PreK	Kindergarten	Grade 1	Grade 2	Grade 3	Grade 4	Grade 5	Course 1	Course 2	Course 3	Pre-Algebra	Algebra 1	Geometry
Temperature (Celsius, Fahrenheit)		○	○	◐	●	●	●	●	●	●	●	●	

Time	PreK	Kindergarten	Grade 1	Grade 2	Grade 3	Grade 4	Grade 5	Course 1	Course 2	Course 3	Pre-Algebra	Algebra 1	Geometry
Morning, afternoon, evening	○	◐	◐	●	●	●							
Calendar	○	◐	●	●	●	●	●						
Tell time, digital/analog		○	◐	●	●	●	●	●					
Estimate time		○	●	●	●	●	●	●					
Elapsed time				○	○	◐	●	●					
Order events		○	◐	●	●	●	●						
Units of time		○	○	◐	●	●	●	●					

Money	PreK	Kindergarten	Grade 1	Grade 2	Grade 3	Grade 4	Grade 5	Course 1	Course 2	Course 3	Pre-Algebra	Algebra 1	Geometry
Recognize and count coins			◐	●	●	●	●						
Compare money amounts			◐	●	◐	●	●						
Find values of coins			◐	◐	●	●	●						
Make change					◐	●	●						
Fractions, decimals, and money					◐	●	●						

Measurement

Measurement	PreK	Kindergarten	Grade 1	Grade 2	Grade 3	Grade 4	Grade 5	Course 1	Course 2	Course 3	Pre-Algebra	Algebra 1	Geometry
Measurement Formulas and Techniques													
Use formulas					●	●	●	●	●	●	●	●	●
Length													
Perimeter of rectangle				●	●	●	●	●	●	●	●	●	●
Circumference of circle								●	●	●	●	●	●
Area and Surface Area													
Compare and order areas	●	●	●	●	●	●							
Estimate area				●	●	●							
Area of rectangle, square				●	●	●	●	●	●	●	●	●	●
Area of parallelogram						●	●	●	●	●	●	●	●
Area of triangle							●	●	●	●	●	●	●
Area of trapezoid								●	●	●	●	●	●
Area of circle								●	●	●	●	●	●
Area of composite figures							●	●	●	●	●	●	●
Surface area of cube, rectangular prism						●	●	●	●	●	●	●	●
Surface area of cylinder								●	●	●	●	●	●
Surface area of cone, pyramid, sphere										●	●	●	●
Volume													
Volume of cube, rectangular prism						●	●	●	●	●	●	●	●
Volume of cylinder									●	●	●	●	●
Volume of cone, pyramid, sphere										●	●	●	●
Angle measurement in degrees							●	●	●	●	●	●	●

● Introduce   ● Develop   ● Reinforce   ● Maintain and Apply   ● Prerequisite Skills

	PreK	Kindergarten	Grade 1	Grade 2	Grade 3	Grade 4	Grade 5	Course 1	Course 2	Course 3	Pre-Algebra	Algebra 1	Geometry
Precision and significant digits												◐	
Indirect measurement								◐	●	●	●	●	●

Geometry

	PreK	Kindergarten	Grade 1	Grade 2	Grade 3	Grade 4	Grade 5	Course 1	Course 2	Course 3	Pre-Algebra	Algebra 1	Geometry
Plane and Solid Shapes													
Identify attributes of plane shapes	○	◐	●	●	●	●	●	●	●	●	●	●	●
Identify attributes of solid shapes	○	◐	●	●	●	●	●	●	●	●	●	●	●
Classify and describe properties of plane shapes	○	◐	●	●	●	●	●	●	●	●	●	●	●
Classify and describe properties of solid shapes	○	◐	●	●	●	●	●	●	●	●	●	●	●
Relate plane and solid figures	○	◐	●	●	●	●	●	●	●	●	●	●	●
Lines, line segments, rays					◐	●	●	●	●	●	●	●	●
Parallel, perpendicular lines					◐	●	●	●	●	●	●	●	◐
Classify and measure angles					◐	●	●	●	●	●	●	●	◐
Angle relationships								◐	●	●	●	●	●
Identify and define polygons		○	◐	◐	●	●	●	●	●	●	●	●	●
Classify quadrilaterals					◐	●	●	●	●	●	●	●	●
Classify triangles					◐	●	●	●	●	●	●	●	●
Sum of angles in a triangle								◐	●	●	●	●	●
Sum of angles of polygons								◐	●	◐	●	●	●

Scope and Sequence

Geometry	PreK	Kindergarten	Grade 1	Grade 2	Grade 3	Grade 4	Grade 5	Course 1	Course 2	Course 3	Pre-Algebra	Algebra 1	Geometry
Parts of circles							●	●	●	●	●	●	●
Congruent figures				●	●	●	●	●	●	●	●	●	●
Similar figures							●	●	●	●	●	●	●
Corresponding parts							●	●	●	●	●	●	●
Scale drawings								●	●	●	●	●	●
Right triangles and parts								●	●	●	●	●	●
Pythagorean Theorem								●	●	●	●	●	●
Right triangle trigonometry													●

Coordinate Geometry	PreK	Kindergarten	Grade 1	Grade 2	Grade 3	Grade 4	Grade 5	Course 1	Course 2	Course 3	Pre-Algebra	Algebra 1	Geometry
Position and direction	●	●	●	●	●	●	●						
Graph ordered pairs			●	●	●	●	●	●	●	●	●	●	●
Horizontal, vertical distance on a grid			●	●	●	●	●	●	●	●	●	●	●
Distance formula											●	●	●
Graph linear equations								●	●	●	●	●	●
Slope								●	●	●	●	●	●
Slope-intercept form of line								●	●	●	●	●	●
Point-slope form of line												●	●
Slope of parallel, perpendicular lines												●	●

Transformations and Symmetry	PreK	Kindergarten	Grade 1	Grade 2	Grade 3	Grade 4	Grade 5	Course 1	Course 2	Course 3	Pre-Algebra	Algebra 1	Geometry
Translations (slide)					●	●	●	●	●	●	●	●	●
Reflections (flip)					●	●	●	●	●	●	●	●	●

● Introduce   ● Develop   ● Reinforce   ● Maintain and Apply   ● Prerequisite Skills

	PreK	Kindergarten	Grade 1	Grade 2	Grade 3	Grade 4	Grade 5	Course 1	Course 2	Course 3	Pre-Algebra	Algebra 1	Geometry
Rotations (turn)					◐	●	●		●	●	●	●	●
Dilations									◐	◐		●	●
Transformations on coordinate plane						◐	◐	●	●	●	●	●	●
Symmetry (line and rotation)				○	◐	●			●	●	●	●	●
Tessellations								◐	●		●	●	●

Spatial Reasoning

	PreK	Kindergarten	Grade 1	Grade 2	Grade 3	Grade 4	Grade 5	Course 1	Course 2	Course 3	Pre-Algebra	Algebra 1	Geometry
Draw angles, lines, polygons					○	◐	●	●	●	●			●
Constructions										◐			●
Draw 3-dimensional objects									◐	◐	●		●
Nets					○	●	●	●	●	●			◐

Data Analysis

Sort, Classify

	PreK	Kindergarten	Grade 1	Grade 2	Grade 3	Grade 4	Grade 5	Course 1	Course 2	Course 3	Pre-Algebra	Algebra 1	Geometry
Sort and classify by attribute	○	◐	●	●	●								
Use Venn diagrams		○	◐	●	●	●	●	◐	◐	◐	◐	◐	●

Collect, Organize, and Display Data

	PreK	Kindergarten	Grade 1	Grade 2	Grade 3	Grade 4	Grade 5	Course 1	Course 2	Course 3	Pre-Algebra	Algebra 1	Geometry
Collect data	○	○	◐	◐	●	●	●	●	◐	◐	◐	◐	●
Organize data with a table			◐	◐	●	●	●	●	●	●	●	●	
Organize data with a graph	○	○	◐	◐	●	●	●	◐	◐	◐	◐	●	
Frequency tables; tally charts			◐	◐	●	●	●	●	●	●	●	●	

Scope and Sequence

Data Analysis	PreK	Kindergarten	Grade 1	Grade 2	Grade 3	Grade 4	Grade 5	Course 1	Course 2	Course 3	Pre-Algebra	Algebra 1	Geometry
Surveys		●	◐	◐	●	●	●	●	●	●	●	●	
Samples								○	○	●	●	●	
Random samples								○	◐	●	●	●	
Use sampling to predict								○	◐	●	●	●	

Represent Data	PreK	Kindergarten	Grade 1	Grade 2	Grade 3	Grade 4	Grade 5	Course 1	Course 2	Course 3	Pre-Algebra	Algebra 1	Geometry
Real graphs	●	◐											
Picture graphs, pictograph	●	◐	●	●	●	●	●						
Bar graphs; double bar graphs		●	◐	●	●	●	●	●	●	●	●	●	
Line plots					◐	●	●	●	●	●	●	●	
Circle graphs								◐	●	●	●	●	●
Line graphs							◐	●	●	●	●	●	
Stem-and-leaf plots								◐	●	●	●	●	
Box-and-whisker plots										◐	◐	●	
Histograms									◐	●	●	●	
Scatter plots									◐	●	●	●	
Fitted lines on scatter plots									○	◐	●	●	
Choose an appropriate graph/display							◐	●	●	●	●	●	

Make Inferences and Predictions	PreK	Kindergarten	Grade 1	Grade 2	Grade 3	Grade 4	Grade 5	Course 1	Course 2	Course 3	Pre-Algebra	Algebra 1	Geometry
Use data		●	◐	●	●	●	●	●	●	●	●	●	
Mode		●	●	○	○	●	●	●	●	●	●	●	
Median					◐	●	●	●	●	●	●	●	
Mean							◐	●	●	●	●	●	

○ Introduce ● Develop ● Reinforce ● Maintain and Apply ● Prerequisite Skills

	PreK	Kindergarten	Grade 1	Grade 2	Grade 3	Grade 4	Grade 5	Course 1	Course 2	Course 3	Pre-Algebra	Algebra 1	Geometry
Range						◐	●	●	●	●	●		
Outliers					○	◐	●	●	●	●	●		
Quartiles										◐	●	●	
Misleading graphs and statistics									◐	●	●	●	
Make predictions from graphs					○	○	◐	●	●	●	●	○	
Make predictions from a sample							○	●	●	●	●		

Probability

	PreK	Kindergarten	Grade 1	Grade 2	Grade 3	Grade 4	Grade 5	Course 1	Course 2	Course 3	Pre-Algebra	Algebra 1	Geometry
Certain, probable, impossible		○	○	◐	●	●	○						
Likely and unlikely, compare likelihoods			○	◐	●	●	○						
Predict outcomes					○	◐	●	●	●	●	●	●	
Outcomes and sample space						◐	◐	●	●	●	●	●	
Probability of a simple event						○	◐	●	●	●	●	●	
Complementary events								◐	●	●	●	◐	
Composite events: independent, dependent									◐	●	●	●	
Mutually exclusive or inclusive events, disjoint											◐	●	
Experimental probability						○	◐	●	●	●	●	●	
Theoretical probability						○	◐	●	●	●	●	●	
Probability and ratio								◐	●	●	●	●	
Simulations									◐	●	●	●	
Tree diagrams						◐	◐	●	●	●	●	●	
Fundamental Counting Principle							○	◐	◐	●	●	●	

Scope and Sequence

Data Analysis

Data Analysis	PreK	Kindergarten	Grade 1	Grade 2	Grade 3	Grade 4	Grade 5	Course 1	Course 2	Course 3	Pre-Algebra	Algebra 1	Geometry
Combinations						●	●	◐	●	●	●	●	
Permutations								◐	●	●	●	●	
Probability distributions											◐		

Problem Solving

Strategies and Skills

Strategies and Skills	PreK	Kindergarten	Grade 1	Grade 2	Grade 3	Grade 4	Grade 5	Course 1	Course 2	Course 3	Pre-Algebra	Algebra 1	Geometry
Look for a pattern	●	◐	◐	●	●	●	●	●	●	●	●	●	●
Act it out, use objects, use simulation		●	◐	●	●	●	●	●	●	●	◐	●	●
Guess and check		●	●	◐	●	●	●	●	●	●	●	●	●
Draw a picture or diagram		●	◐	●	●	●	●	●	●	●	●	●	●
Make a table		●	●	●	●	●	●	●	●	●	●	●	●
Make a graph		●	●	●	◐	●	●	●	●	●	●	●	●
Make a list				◐	◐	●	●	●	●	●	●	●	●
Make a model	●			◐	●	●	●	●	●	●	●	●	●
Work backward				●	◐	●	●	●	●	●	●	●	●
Use logical reasoning		●	◐	◐	●	●	●	●	●	●	●	◐	●
Use a four-step plan		●	◐	●	●	●	●	●	●	●	●	●	●
Choose a strategy		◐	◐	●	●	●	●	●	●	●	●	●	●
Choose an operation			●	●	●	●	●	●	●	●	●	●	●
Check for reasonableness		●	●	◐	●	●	●	●	●	●	●	●	●

○ Introduce ● Develop ● Reinforce ● Maintain and Apply ● Prerequisite Skills

	PreK	Kindergarten	Grade 1	Grade 2	Grade 3	Grade 4	Grade 5	Course 1	Course 2	Course 3	Pre-Algebra	Algebra 1	Geometry
Write a number sentence			○	◐	●	●	●						
Write an equation						◐	●	●	●	●	●	●	●
Use formulas					○	●	●	●	●	●	●	●	●
Decide whether to estimate or compute					◐	●	●	●	●	●	●	●	●
Identify missing or extra information					◐	●	●						
Solve multi-step problems						◐	●	●	●	●	●	●	●
Conduct a poll or survey			○	◐	●	●	●	●	●	●	●	●	●
Solve a simpler problem					◐	●	●	●	●	●	●	●	●

Mathematical Reasoning and Justification

	PreK	Kindergarten	Grade 1	Grade 2	Grade 3	Grade 4	Grade 5	Course 1	Course 2	Course 3	Pre-Algebra	Algebra 1	Geometry
Use mathematical reasoning		○	○	◐	●	●	●	●	●	●	●	●	●
Use Venn diagrams		○	◐	●	●	●	●	●	●	●	●	●	●
Explain, justify, and defend reasoning			○	◐	●	●	●	●	●	●	●	●	●
Check validity of calculated results		○	◐	●	●	◐	●	●	●	●	●	●	●
Create problems					◐	●	●	●	●	●	●	●	●
Write informal mathematical arguments			○	◐	●	●	●	●	●	●	●	◐	●
Make and test conjectures, counterexamples						○	○	◐	◐	●	●	●	●
Inductive reasoning								◐	●	●	●	●	●
Deductive reasoning								◐	●	●	●	●	●
Develop a proof: paragraph, algebraic, coordinate, indirect												◐	●

Literature Support

Contents

Linking to Literacy

The Read-Aloud Anthology is intended to introduce and reinforce the concept(s) being introduced in each chapter of the Student Edition. As you read each selection aloud, model fluent, proficient oral reading. (Students may follow along as you read; text for each read-aloud selection can be found in *Hands-On Activity Tools and Resources*.) You might elect to have students partner-read or silently read these selections, depending on time allowed for the activity and the reading levels of the students in your classroom.

The following summaries relate how you might use each section of the teacher support found throughout the Read-Aloud Anthology in your classroom.

Reading in Math

- Use this section to underscore the relationship between the read-aloud selection for a given chapter to the math concept contained in that chapter.

- The support in this section might also reinforce common reading and language arts skills derived from the chapter's selection. For example, phonemic awareness or phonics skills identified in the piece might be identified and explained for primary students. For upper elementary students, this section might introduce common language arts elements, such as parts of speech or figurative language. You might also use this section to assess students' prior knowledge of the main ideas in the read-aloud piece.

Math Vocabulary

- Use this section to integrate and/or review math vocabulary from the read-aloud selection with the math vocabulary found in the *Student Edition*.

- Most support written for this section refers to the Vocabulary graphic organizer found in *Hands-On Activity Tools and Resources*. This graphic organizer is based on the Frayer Model (Frayer, 1969).

- You might wish to model using this graphic organizer initially, gradually allowing students to complete charts independently later in the year. Primary students will likely use drawings to complete the four fields, while upper-elementary students should use phrases and words to complete theirs. You may wish to have students organize these pages in Math Vocabulary Folders for their reference throughout the school year and as a study guide for spring testing.

Math Comprehension

- Use this section to help students connect comprehension of the read-aloud selection to comprehension of the chapter's math content. This might be in the form of teacher-led discussion, a brief activity, or completion of a graphic organizer.

- Students should be expected to demonstrate familiarity and knowledge of the math chapter's content and connect it through an activity. For example, they might use the Venn diagram graphic organizer to compare two distinct math concepts in a selection, or they could complete the 4-column chart graphic organizer to demonstrate multiple approaches to problem solving.

Anonymous

A group of moose, whose skulls were thick,
attempted some arithmetic.
Of course their efforts were no use,
their minds were but the minds of moose.
Addition was a hopeless act,
and likewise, they could not subtract.
Devoid of acumen and wit,
they could not multiply a bit.

Division was beyond them too,
they clearly did not have a clue.
Percentages just gave them pains,
and fractions overtaxed their brains.
Those addlepated moose were vexed,
uncomprehending, and perplexed.
"We're through with math," they sadly sighed.
"Those numbers have us moostified."

Reading in Math

- Have students skim the poem for unfamiliar vocabulary.

- In the poem, there are two different spelling patterns used for the ending sound "shun." Have students work with partners to locate and underline these spelling patterns (*tion, sion*).

- Provide students with time to brainstorm other words that end with this sound pattern.

Math Vocabulary

- If the moose are more familiar with mathematical definitions, they may fare better with arithmetic. Tell students to create an arithmetic encyclopedia for the moose using chapter vocabulary. Write vocabulary on slips of paper and have either individual, or pairs of, students choose them at random.

- Students will use these words to create Vocabulary charts to include in the class "Moosclopedia."

Math Comprehension

- The moose in the poem are unable to perform simple calculations. Tell students to help make the moose more math savvy. They will choose a chapter concept, such as prime factorization, or order of operations, that they will explain to the moose. Have students use a Sequence chart to describe the steps they used.

by Lenda Hill

Mr. Mean isn't angry
  he's just misunderstood
Just take the time to interpret him,
And all the neighbors in his hood—
  Ms. Median, Mode Jr., and Dr. Range
They're a fun crowd
  always looking for a change

I'll give you a glimpse of Mr. Mean's
  personality,
And then you can find him in all the data
  that you see.
He's not mean, he's just shy
Mr. Mean is even quiet around me!

Mr. Mean is a straightforward guy
He doesn't want a lot of numbers
  when one is enough to get by.
That is why he adds them together
  And then averages them out
It's his way of summing things up—
I know this beyond any doubt.

So when you meet Mr. Mean,
  give him a chance.
Who knows?
He might make a good date to
  your school's next dance!

Reading in Math

- As a class, echo read the poem to practice fluent and expressive reading.

- Pair students together and assign them the task of summarizing the poem. First, students should read the poem silently to themselves. Then, they will work alone and write summaries. When finished, have students compare their summaries. What important ideas were left out? Was everything in the proper sequence?

- As a class discuss the components of an effective summary.

Math Vocabulary

- Discuss with students the characters presented in the poem. Ask students to choose a character for their Vocabulary charts. Encourage them to use vocabulary from the chapter in their charts.

Math Comprehension

- Distribute Venn diagrams to students and ask them to entitle the two outermost regions "Mr. Mean" and "Me." Ask students to compare and contrast themselves with the poem's main character. Alternatively, students could compare and contrast Mr. Mean with a character from a book they are reading.

- Students may create a poem like "Mr. Mean," describing either themselves or the character they choose from a text.

Reading in Math

- Review parts of speech with students by having them highlight nouns, verbs, and adjectives from the poem for inclusion in a student-made chart.

- Many words in the poem were not highlighted. Ask students what part of speech they are. Have students look them up using any type of dictionary to determine which part of speech they are. (You may need to review with students where in the definition the part of speech is mentioned.)

Math Vocabulary

- The poem tells the reader "a meter's a hundred centimeters." What part of a meter is one centimeter? Students should suggest that it is $\frac{1}{100}$ or .01 of a meter.

- Have students review decimals by creating a Vocabulary chart using "decimals" as its focus.

Math Comprehension

- Provide students with a list of addition and subtraction problems, both involving decimals. Using front-end estimation, students should estimate the answers and record the problems on a Two-Column chart. For example, if a student reads the problem 34.59 — 29.43, he or she should predict, using front-end estimation, that the answer would be less than ten and record the problem in the correct column.

Anonymous

A century is a hundred years.
A dollar is a hundred cents.
A meter's a hundred centimeters.
Is all this starting to make some sense?

'Cause "cent" can mean one hundred
in some words that we all know.
Like, a centipede has a hundred legs
that keep him on the go!

By Lee Bennett Hopkins

Decimal point

meteors

streak

through

the night—

Fractions

of moonbeams

gleam

white-bright—

Percentages

of stars

seem

to multiply—

in the

finite

dramatic

mathematic-filled

sky.

Reading in Math

- Have students pick their favorite stanza to sketch. Ask them to reread their stanza to help them create sketches of their visualizations.

- Below their drawings, have students write other words related to their sketches. Encourage them to think of words related to mathematics. After students have brainstormed words for a few moments, they will choose some to include in an original poem about the sky or another related topic, such as the seemingly infinite sea.

Math Vocabulary

- *Fractions of moonbeams shimmer brightly* and *stars seem to multiply* as the poem's author gazes into the sky. Ask students to choose vocabulary from the chapter that is connected to both fractions and multiplying to create their vocabulary charts. Somewhere on their charts, they should cite how the words or phrases are associated with both concepts.

Math Comprehension

- Ask students to solve a problem referenced in the chapter, such as finding the greatest common factor or determining simplest form.

- Have students use the Sequence chart to explain the steps they took to find the answer.

Reading in Math

Have students identify and highlight verbs from the poem.

- As students share their highlighted verbs, record them on the board. Ask the class if they can think of a way to organize the list. Students may notice that some of the verbs end in *-ed, -ing, -s,* while others have no ending. Suggest to students that the verbs be organized by their tenses.

- Distribute chart paper to small groups of students and assign them the task of creating a three-column chart of verb tenses.

Math Vocabulary

- The poem's narrator contemplates unlike fractions at the poem's conclusion. As a class, explore the phrases "like fractions" and "unlike fractions" using Vocabulary charts.

- After students have finished their charts, discuss the usefulness of both types of fractions. When, in real life, will students use like fractions? (Sample answer: adding different quantities of time, such as two half-hours and one quarter-hour.) **What about unlike fractions?** (Sample answer: following a recipe.)

Math Comprehension

- Distribute a Two-Column chart to each student. Entitle the left column "Unlike Fractions", and the right column "Like Fractions." Have students number from one to five in the left column. Then, suggest two or more fractions for them to record by each number. For example, next to number one, have students write: $\frac{4}{6}$, $\frac{2}{9}$, and $\frac{1}{2}$. In the right column, they will write like

By Lenda Hill

Dividing things into pieces and parts…

Working with fractions, it seems, is an art.

Numerator and denominator; subtract or add

All of that math vocabulary spinning in my head.

I wonder: *When will I use fractions in real life?*

Then I think of sharing Mother's apple pie—such strife!

I'm reminded of the family showdown over each slice.

(If I get to eat more than my brothers, that would be quite nice!)

With more brothers than sisters, some boys may have to do without.

Perhaps they'll eat smaller pieces so that no one has an empty mouth!

Four pieces for them, two pieces for us (you see, I'm one in a set of twins)

I wonder if they'll notice the largest denominator doesn't always win?!

Literature Support

Reading in Math

- Display the poem to the class and give students time to read the poem to themselves.

- Share examples of personification with the class (e.g., "the sun smiled down upon the earth" or "the rain kissed the sidewalks of the small town"). Have students choose a classroom object and write a sentence in which that object is personified.

- Challenge students to rewrite the poem from the decimal point's perspective. Encourage students to personify the decimal point by giving it human qualities.

Math Vocabulary

- In this chapter, students learn that large numbers can be expressed in scientific notation with the use of a coefficient, the base (10), and an exponent. Remind students that in the coefficient, the decimal is written after the first digit. Write three large numbers on the board (e.g., 45,000,000,000) and ask volunteers to write these numbers using scientific notation. Afterwards, write some numbers using scientific notation and ask students to write the actual numbers.

- Have students work independently or with partners to create Vocabulary charts to define scientific notation.

Math Comprehension

- Give students a Sequence chart upon which to write the steps involved in writing a number in scientific notation. Advise them to use both words and numbers in each step of their explanation.

By Lenda Hill

Decimal point, decimal point
   Can I shift you to the right?
I need more change in my pocket
   For popcorn at the movie tonight.

Decimal point, decimal point
   Will you be my best friend?
I'll multiply you by a power of ten
   And shift you to the very end!

Decimal point, decimal point
   Your meaning is so clear
With each purchase at the mall,
   the smaller your left side—Tears!

Decimal point, decimal point
   I did my chores on time.
So Mom and Dad passed out my allowance.
   What's this?—Not an extra dime!

Reading in Math

- In the poem, the last two lines mention a possible cause and effect relationship (low temperatures could cause snow to fall, which, in turn, could keep students at home for a snow day). Ask students to think about events that could be caused by different temperatures. List students' ideas on the board.

- Students will choose one of the suggested ideas and incorporate it into a written piece. They can choose from various formats, such as a short story, a poem, a comic strip, etc.

Math Vocabulary

- Ask students to infer the starting temperature in the poem by identifying clues (e.g., it might snow, 27 degrees is added to the number when the sun warms the sky, 36 degrees is subtracted when the temperature plummets at night). They can make inferences by writing equations using the clues given. For example, students may infer that the starting temperature is not higher than 5 degrees because $5 + 27 = 32$, which is the freezing point of water and snow cannot fall at warmer temperatures.

- Have students create Vocabulary charts to define "equation." Encourage them to think of different types of equations, including algebraic equations and those involving inverse operations.

Math Comprehension

- Distribute Venn diagrams to students so that they may compare numerical equations and algebraic equations. Ask students to consider when it would be useful to use each type of equation.

By Lenda Hill

Positive, negative, rounded or straight.

Only so much can one person take.

Greater, less, whole or part.

Where do I end? Depends on where it starts.

27 to the right with the sun in the sky.

36 back left as the nighttime comes by.

The weather forecast says no warming all day.

Perhaps that means snow, and at home we'll stay.

Sherlock Holmes Solves a Math Problem

Anonymous

Reading in Math

Ask students to mark up the text as they read. Each time they encounter a new fact, they will highlight it and write a "+" next to it. When students read something they don't understand, they will highlight it and write a "?" beside it.

- Have students locate words with inflectional endings. After students have circled the words, create a chart that divides the highlighted words into columns. For example, in the "-ing" column, words such as "doing," "solving," and "challenging" would appear.

- Discuss how each ending changes the meaning of words. Encourage students to list other words that contain the same inflectional endings in the appropriate columns.

Math Vocabulary

- Holmes used proportions to ascertain the height of a 64 feet pole's shadow. Assign students the task of determining how long a rope must be for 20 people to play tug-of-war. If students know that four people can play with a rope that is 10 feet long, they can determine the length of rope (50 feet) needed for 20 to play.

- Have students complete a Vocabulary chart focusing on proportions. Encourage them to create their own proportions for inclusion in the Examples region.

Math Comprehension

- Refer to the chart created by the class and have them choose 10 to 15 words from the list. Using a Three-Column chart, students will list the base or root words in the first column, the inflectional ending in the second column, and

Doing mathematics is much like solving a mystery. If a math problem is challenging, you may look for clues, try different approaches, or start by gathering data. Above all, you need logical reasoning.

One of the most famous logical reasoners of all is the fictional character Sherlock Holmes. In the stories and novels of Arthur Conan Doyle, Holmes and his loyal friend Watson solve a wide variety of mysteries. Holmes considers detection a science. When Watson reports their adventures, Holmes can be impatient if Watson emphasizes the exciting drama more than the pure logic.

"The Adventure of Musgrave Ritual" is a typical Sherlock Holmes story. In the story, facts seem to lead to a hidden treasure. Holmes realizes that he needs to find the end of the shadow of an elm tree at a certain time. However, the elm has been cut down. Another character remembers that the elm was 64 feet tall. So Holmes uses a six-foot fishing pole and a little math. The six-foot pole casts a shadow nine feet long. Holmes draws a diagram like the one below, showing the pole and its shadow. Holmes knows that the shadow of the tree will be proportionally as long as the shadow of the pole. Doing a little math, he figures that the shadow of the 64-foot tree was 96 feet long.

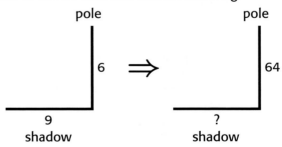

The next time you have a difficult math problem to do, remember Sherlock Holmes. He found his math skills useful in his work. Someday you may too.

Visualizing Percentages

Anonymous

Many people find percentages difficult. A percentage is different from a number such as 25. You can imagine 25 golf balls. Or you might think of 25 dollars or 25 feet. Twenty-five of something is easy to visualize. You can picture it in your mind.

It is harder to form a mental picture of 25 percent. A percentage compares things. It compares the number to 100. Think of the percentage sign (%) as meaning "out of 100." Thus 25 percent means "25 out of 100." This may help you understand what 25 percent means. But it doesn't help you make a mental picture of 25 percent.

To picture 25 percent, you need an example. That is because 25 percent can mean different things. Getting 25 percent of a small number is different from getting 25 percent of a large number. For example, 25 percent of $83 is much less than 25 percent of $8,300.

Is there a way to picture an example like 25 percent of $83? One way is to sketch two bars, both of the same length. One bar, the percent bar, has 100 units. The other, the number bar, has 83 units.

Notice that the sketch has a <u>vertical</u> line. This line goes through 25 on the percent bar and hits the number bar at about 21. So the diagram helps you "see" a percentage. It shows that 25 percent of $83 is about $21.

Making bar diagrams for percentages can assist you in comprehending what the percentages mean. Your diagrams need not be beautiful; in fact, they can be rough. They are also a useful way to doublecheck answers you arrive at with a calculator.

Reading in Math

- Have students skim both stanzas to look for base or root words. Ask students to highlight and share them with the class. Share with students that affixes and inflectional endings alter the meanings of base words.

- Choose a base word suggested by students (e.g., known) and add affixes and inflectional endings to make new words that make sense. Invite students to choose base words from the poem and create new words by adding affixes and or inflectional endings.

Math Vocabulary

- The poem's author discusses paths that are still undiscovered in our world. In the geometric world, there are several types of paths. Lines, line segments, and rays are all types of straight paths, and they form many figures, such as angles, polygons, and three-dimensional figures.

- Students may choose any of the chapter's vocabulary words for their charts.

Math Comprehension

- Given Three-Column charts with the columns labeled "Line Segments," "Lines," and "Rays," students will identify which geometric vocabulary should be listed in each column. For example, triangles and quadrilaterals are made up of line segments and should be listed in that column. After students are done sorting chapter vocabulary, encourage them to list real-world objects on the chart. Sunlight could be listed as a type of ray and the edges of classroom posters as line segments.

By Arthur St. John Adcock

Come, let us go a-roaming!
The world is all our own,
And half its paths are still untrod,
And half its joys unknown.

The way that leads to winter
Will lead to summer too,
For all roads end in other roads
Where we may start anew.

Literature Support

Literature Support

Reading in Math

- Instruct students to mark up the text as they read. They can use the following symbols to code their understanding of the text: 1) when a new fact is learned, students will highlight it and write a "+", 2) when students encounter a fact they already know, they will highlight it and write a "★", 3) when students come across something they don't understand, they will highlight it and code it with a "?."

- Invite students to share new facts or questions they had about the text. Discuss with students strategies they can use when they don't understand something.

Math Vocabulary

- Challenge students to calculate pi using mathematical tools. Distribute to small groups a variety of tools, such as: calculators, compasses, rulers, string, protractors, etc. Their task will be to use appropriate tools to calculate pi (possible method: use compass to draw a circle and measure its diameter using a ruler; find the circle's circumference by using a piece of string to trace its outline and measure the string's length).

- After sharing their solutions, students will work in their same small groups to complete Vocabulary charts centering on "circumference."

Math Comprehension

- Instead of explaining their method for calculating pi, students can explain their mathematical thinking using the boxes of a sequence chart. Have students use time-and-order words to enhance the flow of their writing.

Anonymous

You may have a calculator with a pi key. This key shows the symbol π, which is a letter from the Greek alphabet. Why is π on one of the calculator keys?

Pi is a number that shows how parts of a circle relate to each other. To understand pi, imagine a circle. Now imagine a line that cuts the circle in half. This line is the diameter. To find a value for pi, use a soup can. The top or bottom of the can is a circle. Put a string around the circular part and measure it. The measurement shows the circumference of the circle, or the distance around it. Now measure the diameter of the can. Divide the circumference by the diameter to find the value for pi.

The value of pi is a constant. It never changes. It doesn't matter how big a circle is. When you divide the circumference by the diameter, you'll get pi. But what number does pi equal? For any circle, dividing the circumference by the diameter will give 3.14 or $\frac{22}{7}$. This is the value of pi.

For thousands of years, people have worked on finding more and more <u>precise</u> values for pi. You may have used 3.14 as the value in a math class. A more precise value is 3.1415926535897931. In 1844 a German man spent two months finding the first 200 digits of pi. In 1947, D. F. Ferguson raised the number of digits to 808.

Today, using computers, people have found hundreds of millions of digits. Since pi is an irrational number, the digits will never repeat in a pattern. So people who are fascinated can keep working on pi. There will never be a last digit for it.

CHAPTER 1 Use Place Value

Lesson 1-1 (p. 17)

One Riddle One Answer
by Lauren Thompson

- Discuss the importance of place value in the riddle.

- Play Guess My Number with the class.

- Secretly write down a number.

- Indicate the number of digits in the number.

- Label column 2 as "Number of Correct Digits", column 3 is labeled "Digits in Correct Place Value".

- A student guesses a number, the leader writes it in column 1 and completes columns 2 and 3. Request another guess.

- Continue until the number is guessed.

- Discuss with the students how column 3 helped refine their guesses.

Lesson 1-2 (p. 20)

How Much is a Million ?
by David M. Schwartz

- Read the book.

- Ask students which is larger, 10 or 1? 100 or 10,000?

- Then give teams of students digit cards 0–9 and comparison cards, <, >, =.

- Have teams form two numbers such as 237 and 273.

- Have them add the comparison card between the numerals.

- Ask them to reverse the numerals and make any other changes needed.

Lesson 1-3 (p. 24)

How Much is a Million?
By David M. Schwartz

- Discuss the four-step problem-solving plan, write the number and challenge students to use the plan to complete a "million" problem.

- After reading have 3 groups of students work together using the four-step problem-solving plan to set up how they will find out if there are more or less than a million seconds in a day, a week, and a month (30 days). 1 day = 24 hours = 86,400 seconds; 1 week = 7 days = 168 hours = 604,800 seconds; 30 days = 720 hours = 43,200 minutes = 25,920,000 seconds

Lesson 1-4 (p. 28)

Math Man by Teri Daniels

- "Math man" is Garth who works at the Mighty Mart where all the customers like the way he adds prices in his head – uses mental math.

- On the 4th and 5th pages from the end of the story there are the money amounts Garth added with the totals of each basket's contents.

- Divide students into three groups and assign a basket to each group. Have students place the prices of the items in their assigned baskets in order from least to greatest and find the difference between the highest priced item and the lowest priced item.

Literature Support

Lesson 1-5 (p. 32)

Alexander, Who Used to be Rich Last Sunday
by Judith Viorst

- Discuss the different amounts of money that Alexander spent.

- Equate the money to decimals. Show students $2.56 and ask someone to read it. Then show 2.56 and ask some one to read it. Discuss how many dimes and how many pennies and make the connection to decimal place value.

- Have students use Base 10 blocks to show a decimal number and then use coins to show the equivalent amount.

- Have students build various decimals with Base 10 blocks and write the decimal number.

Lesson 1-6 (p. 36)

Little Numbers and Pictures that Show Just How Little They Are! by Edward Packard

- Read the book just up to the pages with the one thousandth on them.

- Ask students which is larger, 0.10 or 0.01? 0.01 or 0.001?

- Then give each student two cards with decimal numbers on them (0.2, 0.67, 0.003, etc). Ask them to use cards with <, >, = to compare the two cards.

- Then ask them to reverse the numbers and explain if they will leave the sign the same or not.

Lesson 1-7 (p. 42)

Math Man by Teri Daniels

- Tell the story to the point that *"the scanners went kaput…"*(page 17).

- Read the next page without showing the comments from the mice.

- Write the amounts on the board and the total the cashier gave. Ask the students what's wrong with it.

- Discuss the importance of the decimal point.

- Give the students 6.13, 16, 6.3, 6, and 16.457 to put in order from least to greatest.

- Ask them what they used to order the numbers? Decimal point? Place value?

2 Add and Subtract Whole Numbers and Decimals

CHAPTER

Lesson 2-1 (p. 61)

Coyotes All Around by Stuart J. Murphy

- Read the book and ask the students if they think the Coyote was clever?

- Have a student explain how the coyote added so fast.

- Revisit pp. 20 –21.

- Give the students the same list of numbers to round: 11, 13, 27, 2.

- See if they agree with Clever Coyote.

- Give the students the set of numbers from page 29 to see if they once again agree with the coyote: 24, 18, 25, 12.

Lesson 2-2 (p. 64)

Sold! A Mathematics Adventure by Nathan Zimelman

- After reading the book discuss how the boy could have found out about how much he was buying without using his calculator.

- Go back through the book and have the students round each amount and give an estimated total.

Lesson 2-3 (p. 68)

Spaghetti and Meatballs for All by Marilyn Burns

- Read the story. Stop throughout to ask students problem-solving questions. For example, How many tables will they need? Why is it a problem that they are pushing tables together?

- After reading, discuss problem solving strategies.

- **How did Mrs. Comfort figure out how to arrange the tables? What other strategies do you know?**

- Give students the following problem to work on in small groups: *"Mrs. Comfort wanted to put flowers on each table. She had twice as many tulips as she had roses. There were 8 more carnations than tulips. There where 48 lilies, which was twice as many carnations. How many roses did Mrs. Comfort need to purchase? How many of each flower should she put at each of the 8 tables?"*

- Discuss strategies students used.

Lesson 2-4 (p. 70)

The Rajah's Rice: A Mathematical Folktale from India by David Barry

- Read the story *The Rajah's Rice* aloud to the class and discuss what happened as the Raja filled up the checkerboard with rice.

- Have the students draw a row of seven boxes like the one below for each day of the week.

Mon	Tues	Wed	Thurs	Fri	Sat	Sun
12	24	48	96	192	384	768

- Ask them to find out how much rice they would have if they started with twelve grains on Monday and it doubled each day until Sunday.

Lesson 2-6 (p. 80)

Pigs Will be Pigs by Amy Axelrod

- As you read the story of *Pigs Will Be Pigs* have students keep a running total on their paper. Have a scribe at the board taking dictation from the class.

- As money is found by the pigs, have the students add it to the previous subtotal. The scribe does not add until the students add, and then tell what digit goes in the ones place, tens place, tenths place, etc.

- Have the students check their total with the author's at the end of the book.

Lesson 2-7 (p. 84)

Math Man by Teri Daniels

- Read *Math Man* aloud to the class and discuss how he was able to add all the prices mentally. Return to page 10 that begins with "How much is a bigger pumpkin?".

- Write the following problems on the board:
  $2.40 + $1.20 = $3.60 or 6 lbs + 3 lbs = 9 lbs

- Ask students if they can mentally solve the following problems:

  - $1.20 + $2.40 or 3 lbs + 6 lbs

  - Explain that problems like this are easy because of the commutative property.

- Write the following problem on the board:

  ($1.20 + $1.60) + $2.00 = $4.80

- Ask students to answer this question mentally:

  - ($2.00 + $1.20) + $1.60

  - Explain that problems like this are easy because of the associative property.

Lesson 2-8 (p. 88)

Math Man by Teri Daniels

- Read the story about Garth, the *Math Man* at the Mighty Mart, focusing on these pages:

  - p. 8 – Ask students to show another way to compute an equal number of snack cakes for each of five kids.

  - p. 9 – Ask students to show a different way to determine the amount of Marnie's money. group like coin denominations first, then add total amounts

  - p. 19 – Ask students to use mental math to find the cost of the three items and have them explain their strategies. $1.50 and $3.50 are $5 and $1.30 more is $6.30

CHAPTER 3 Multiply Whole Numbers

Lesson 3-1 (p. 103)

The Best of Times
by Greg Tang

- After reading the riddle, divide the class into 3 groups. Each group MUST use the materials given to them: Group 1. calculator, Group 2. paper and pencil, Group 3. mental math, using the rule from the riddle.

- Give the students several "times" 10 problems such as 7×10, 18×10, 72×10 and 100×10 one at a time.

- Have students raise their hands as soon as they get the answer. Discuss which group arrives at the answers first and why.

Lesson 3-2 (p. 108)

Math for All Seasons
by Greg Tang

- Read the riddle and have students look at the acorn groupings.

- How many groups of three do you see? Groups of two?

- Show them a "short cut" to writing three groups of 3 and three groups of 2: 3 groups of (3 + 2) or 3(3 + 2)

- Draw another pattern of two sets of 4 circles and two sets of 5 squares.

- Ask the students how they could write this. 2(4 + 5)

Lesson 3-3 (p. 112)

Pigs Will be Pigs: Fun with Math and Money
by Amy Axelrod

- Show students the menu.

- Tell them you want to order 4 specials. ABOUT how much will that cost?

- Discuss rounding the price and then multiplying.

- Let students make other choices on the menu and then order multiple amounts of the item.

Lesson 3-4 (p. 116)

Amanda Bean's Amazing Dream
by Cindy Neuschwander

- Read the book up to the point where Amanda sees the grandmas knitting sweaters.

- Ask the students how they would find out how many sleeves in all of the sweaters.

- Set a new scenario: Amanda sees 42 grandmas knitting sweaters for the sheep (4 legs). How many "arms" would be in all of those sweaters?

Lesson 3-5 (p. 120)

Beanstalk: The Measure of a Giant by Ann McCallum

- This new version of *Jack and the Beanstalk* has Jack working to adapt the size of his favorite past times to accommodate the giant names Ray.

- On p. 17 Jack draws a diagram to determine that Ray is going to need a checkerboard 5 times bigger than the one Jack usually plays on.

- On p. 28 Jack draws another diagram using ratio to find the height of the beanstalk from the shadow it casts.

- Have students use inch grid paper to draw a diagram showing a one-inch height compared to a height ten times taller.

Lesson 3-6 (p. 122)

Sea Squares by Joy Hulme

- Ask the students what the factors of the next square would be. 11×11

- Show them what the "squares" look like: 1×1, 2×2, 3×3...

- Ask them to draw the 11×11 grid. Do they want to count the total number of squares? What's another way?

- Now let's think about rectangles.

- Ask a student to draw a 2×4 rectangular grid on the board and find the total.

- Now label a rectangle with the factors 23 and 36 and to find the total number of squares.

Lesson 3-7 (p. 126)

My Full Moon is Square by Elinor Pinczes

- Ask pairs of students to arrange 12 color tiles in a rectangle. Describe the rectangles naming all possibilities. Display a representation of each rectangle as it is described. 1×12, 12×1, 2×6, 6×2, 3×4, 4×3

- Discuss how the *factors* of each rectangle are the lengths of the sides. They are multiplied together to give the *product*, or area of the rectangles.

- Cut a model of the 2×6 rectangle out of grid paper.

- Discuss the product is the same no matter how the grid is positioned.

- $2 \times 6 = 12$ and $6 \times 2 = 12$ so, $2 \times 6 = 6 \times 2$.

Lesson 3-8 (p. 132)

Minnie's Diner by Dayle Ann Dodds

- After reading the book, discuss the pattern the McFays used to order their meals (1, 2, 4, 8, 16).

- Pretend the special for the day costs $7.36.

- How much would each son pay? Papa?

- What happens to the decimal point?

CHAPTER 4 Divide Whole Numbers

Lesson 4-1 (p. 149)

A Place for Zero by Angeline Sparagna Lopresti

- Tell the story of Zero's journey up to page 24. Read page 24 to the end of the book.

- Ask the students what happened after 100 was made?

- Ask the students how many groups of 10 would be in 200? 300? 500?

- Write the pattern on the board as a table. Ask students to notice a pattern.

- Ask students to use the pattern to find how many tens are in 650.

Lesson 4-2 (p. 152)

Betcha! by Stuart J. Murphy

- Read the book.

- Tell the students that the boys had $10.00 each to spend at the All Star game.

- Hot dogs cost $4.85 each. How many hot dogs could the boys buy with their money?

- Talk to the students about $4.85 "rounding" to a number that it's close to that could easily divide into $20.00. $20 \div 5$

- Have the students try another scenario: sodas cost $3.68. If they have $8.00 left how many sodas could they buy? $8 \div 4$

Lesson 4-3 (p. 158)

A Remainder of One by Elinor Pinczes

- Discuss the book and why there finally wasn't a remainder of one.

- Ask the students to decide what 16 would need to be divided by to have a remainder of 1 5, 2 7?

- Ask students if 5 is the divisor (amount of sets or objects in a set), what dividend (number divided into) would give a remainder of 2? any number with a 7 or 2 in the ones place

Lesson 4-4 (p. 162)

Cut Down to Size at High Noon: A Math Adventure by Scott Sundby

- Read pages 1–7.

- Discuss how Louie scales down the objects.

- Ask the students to take an arena that is 180 feet × 168 feet and scale it down using 15 feet = 1 foot.

- Ask for the new dimensions. 15 ft × 14 ft

Lesson 4-5 (p. 166)

If You Hopped Like a Frog by David M. Schwartz

- As you read through the story have students look closely at the comparisons and ratios made and displayed by the illustrations.

- Divide students into 4 groups and assign each group the task of determining how far they could walk in a single step if they could take steps ten times longer than they do currently.

- Provide each group with one tape measurer and graph paper for recording their findings.

- The information for each group should be displayed in a table or graph that is organized showing comparisons.

Lesson 4-6 (p. 170)

17 Kings and 42 Elephants by Margaret Mahy

- Read the book and discuss with students how they would determine the amount of elephants each king would be responsible for.

- Discuss the fact that there is a remainder in this problem.

- Guide the students to realize that in the story the Kings are not leaving any elephants behind, so the remainder elephants are important.

- Give other scenarios with remainders and have students decide if the remainder would round down the quotient (cookies filling boxes), round up the quotient (people and seats on a bus) or be significant in some other way.

Lesson 4-7 (p. 174)

Pigs will be Pigs by Amy Axelrod

- Just use the menu in the center of the book.

- Tell students that 2 skinny girls are going to share the special. How much will each pay?

- Then ask students to roll a die to determine how many people will share entrees. The die can be rolled again to determine the number of entrees shared.

- Students should total the entrees and then divide by the amount of people sharing them.

CHAPTER 5 Use Algebraic Expressions

Lesson 5-1 (p. 193)

Once Upon a Dime by Nancy Kelly Allen

- Look at this story as a "tall tale" with money growing on trees.

- Have students use an addition equation to find the total amount of money harvested from the tree before the leaves turned into Chinese dollars, yaun: 100 p (for pennies) + 100 n (for nickels) + 100 d (for dimes) + 100 q (for quarters) + 100 b (for dollar bills.) $141.00

- Then compare that amount with what was produced while the farmer was away in China: 50 p + 50 n + 75 q + 75 p + 100 q + 100 b. $147.50

Lesson 5-2 (p. 196)

If You Made a Million by David M. Schwartz

- On p. 17 the author states that $100 in pennies will be a fifty- foot stack. Ask students if they think the author actually made a fifty-foot stack of pennies.

- He probably made a <u>smaller stack</u>, measured that smaller stack, and then multiplied to determine the total height – he solved a simpler problem.

- Have students check the author's accuracy by making a one-foot stack of pennies, count the number of pennies in the one-foot stack, multiply the number of pennies by 50 (to get a fifty-foot stack) and see if it totals ten-thousand pennies.

Lesson 5-3 (p. 198)

The Librarian Who Measured the Earth by Kathryn Lasky

- This is a story of Erasthothenes, mathematician and librarian for the great library at Alexandria in modern day Egypt, who measured the circumference of Earth to within 200 miles of what we know it is today.

- He used π (3.14) and the formula for circumference: $C = \pi d$ with d representing diameter.

- Provide student partners with cut circles of varied sizes, string, and measuring tapes to 'discover' pi by dividing the measured circumference by the diameter of that circle.

- Have students use the multiplication expression/ formula for circumference to check the circumference of their circles.

Lesson 5-4 (p. 202)

Two of Everything by Lily Toy Hong

- Introduce the book by asking students if they would like a magic pot? Ask them if they think it would be a problem if all of a sudden there were 2 of them.

- Ask students to listen to the book to see what happens to the old man and his magic pot.

- After reading the story, show students the expression $2x = y$. Tell students that the expression represents what happens in the pot. If one man goes in, 2 come out. Ask students what would happen if the man put $10 in. How much would come out? Give students other amounts money for extra practice.

- Ask students what the number sentence would be if every time something went in, 3 came out. $3x = y$ What would the number sentence look like if 10 times as many came out?

Lesson 5-6 (p. 210)

Pizza Counting by Christina Dobson

- Read about the different varieties of pizzas as well as all the different ways a pizza can be sliced on pp. 22–31.

- Have students set up a function table to show how many pizza slices, in fractional format, would be needed if each person ate 3 one-tenth pieces.

- Have students calculate for 2 people, 3 people, 4, 5, 6, 7, 8, 9, and 10 people.

- Discuss the pattern revealed and ask students to determine the number of pizzas needed to feed 20 people with the same conditions: 3 one-tenth slices/person. 6 whole pizzas would be needed.

Lesson 5-7 (p. 218)

Amanda Bean's Amazing Dream
by Cindy Neuschwander

- Amanda Bean discovers that multiplying is a more efficient way to keep track of everything she is trying to count.

- Ask students if it would be easier to count/add, subtract, multiply, or divide to find: the number of shoe laces in the room (count and multiply by two), the number of eyes in the room (count and multiply by two), the number of days in 3 weeks (multiply), the number of half gallons in 6 gallons (multiply by two), the number of 12-person buses needed for a field trip for 36 people (divide 36 by twelve).

CHAPTER 6 Use Equations and Function Tables

Lesson 6-1 (p. 237)

Sir Circumference and the Sword in the Cone
by Cindy Neuschwander

- This story illustrates Euler's Law for geometric solids stating that anytime the number of faces on a geometric solid is added to the number of its vertices and then subtracted from the number of its edges the answer will always be two. (See p. 32)

- Provide students with these geometric solids: cube, pyramid, rectangular prism, and triangular prism. (These can be constructed with paper.)

- Have students recreate the chart on p. 12 and prove Euler's law about polyhedron using addition and subtraction with the given geometric solids.

Lesson 6-2 (p. 244)

The Warlord's Puzzle by Walton Pilegard

- This story is about tangrams, an ancient Chinese puzzle.

- Provide students with the template at the end of the story to make a set of tangrams.

- Have students place the template on inch graph paper before cutting the pieces to determine the area using a multiplication equation: $A = \ell \times w$ (Area = length × width). 5 by 5 square = area of 25 square inches.

- Have students focus on each tangram piece's relationship to the total area: large triangles—$\frac{1}{4}$ the total area; small triangles—$\frac{1}{8}$ of the total area, etc.

Lesson 6-3 (p. 248)

Hottest Coldest Highest Deepest by Steve Jenkins

- Read the story *Hottest Coldest Highest Deepest* and then have the students complete the activity.

  - As you read the story aloud, have a frequency table made with all 7 continents listed. For each country stated in the book, have the students find out which continent the country is on.

  - When you finish reading, and your frequency chart is complete, ask students question based on the data collected. For example, ask how many more times North America is mentioned in the book than Asia.

Continents		
Number	**Tally**	**Frequency**
Africa		
Antarctica		
Asia		
Australia		
Europe		
N. America		
S. America		

Lesson 6-4 (p. 250)

The Fly on the Ceiling: A Math Myth by Dr. Julie Glass

- This myth tells of Rene Descartes discovering the Cartesian Coordinate System and how to use ordered pairs.

- Have students use graph paper to place six small geometric shapes on different points on a 10 × 10 coordinate grid. Be sure the system is numbered on both the x and y-axes from 0 to 10.

- On a separate sheet of paper have students make a list, similar to the one on p. 43, of ordered pairs to locate each shape.

- Have students exchange grid papers to find each other's ordered pairs and then check for agreement.

Lesson 6-5 (p. 254)

How Do You Know What Time It Is? by Robert E. Wells

- A history of time telling devices as well as an explanation of time zones and elapsed time is given in this book.

- Have students construct a horizontal or vertical function table for the number of hours in one day (24), in 2 days (48), in 3 days (72), and on to 10 days (240).

- Provide students with $\frac{1}{2}$ cm. graph paper and have them use the data from their function chart to graph a linear function using the day (1 to 10) as the x coordinate and the hours (24–240) as the y coordinate.

Lesson 6-6 (p. 260)

A Place for Zero: A Math Adventure
by Angeline Sparagna Lopresti

- This story shows a function machine and what happens when zero is used in the rule.

- Graphic displays of the identity property of addition and subtraction (zero added to or subtracted from any number leaves the number unchanged in value) and the zero property of multiplication (any number multiplied by a factor of zero has the product zero) are shown.

- Have students design and display an input/output function machine using addition, subtraction, multiplication, or division with only three trials shown.

- Have students exchange papers and discover each other's rules and fill in the next 3 trials.

CHAPTER 7 Display and Interpret Data

Lesson 7-1 (p. 279)

Counting Jennie by Helena Clare Pittman

- Look at the end of the story to see a list of the quantities of all the items Jennie counted.

- Have students find the median of this data. (The median is the number in the middle of the data arranged from least to greatest. With an even number of numbers, the median is the mean of the two middle numbers.)

- Have students find the mode of the data. (The mode is the number that occurs most often in a set of data – there may not be a mode if no identical data is given.)

Lesson 7-3 (p. 284)

Zooming and Creeping by Barbara Taylor

- Have students arrange the data about the speed of the animals on pp. 6–7 and p. 22. (Human 22 mph, hawk moth 24 mph, ostrich 45 mph, horse 43 mph, cheetah 54 mph, sail fish 62 mph, and diving peregrine falcon 124 mph)

- Using graph paper have students plot the maximum speeds from 22 mph to 124 mph as points and connect the points making a line plot to show the increasing speed of each animal recorded.

- Have students use different data from the book to design a new line plot – see pp. 8–9.

Lesson 7-4 (p. 289)

G is for Googol by David M. Schwartz

- As you read through this alphabet book based on mathematical concepts have students suggest other math concepts for each letter of the alphabet.

- Have students write their first names on a strip of inch graph paper placing one letter in each square and then have them make a horizontal bar graph with their names making comparisons about length, number of letters, identical names, etc.

- Have students speculate if there are more consonants or vowels and which letter of the alphabet is most frequently used in their names and how they can determine this frequency data. tally charts

Lesson 7-5 (p. 294)

A Tree in a Forest by Jan Thornhill

- This story traces the life of a tree in a forest in years but with irregular intervals.

- First have students record the years in a timeline and then discuss how the author uses irregular intervals instead of regular intervals such as 5, 10, 15 years or 10, 20, 30 years.

- Have students show the tree's years of life in a vertical bar graph so that each stage the author writes about is shown in years.

- Students should add some descriptive detail to each recorded number of years so the tree's life can be traced.

Lesson 7-6 (p. 299)

Tiger Math: Learning to Graph From a Baby Tiger by Ann Whitehead Nagda and Cindy Bickel

- This photographic essay traces the growth of two baby tigers using a variety of graph types to display data: bar graphs, double bar graphs, line graphs, double line graphs, and circle graphs.

- Have students measure their height with adding machine tape and then record their heights on the tape in inches or centimeters – tally a consensus vote for the choice of the measurement scale.

- Display the strips of adding machine tape in a vertical bar graph to make comparisons about height that is greater than, less than, or equal to another height in the graph.

Lesson 7-7 (p. 306)

Weather by Seymour Simon

- This informational/expository text overview of weather lends itself to a discussion of all types of weather and all the measurements associated with weather forecasting and reporting.

- High and low temperatures are usually displayed in line graphs using degrees as the interval. A double line graph can be used to compare both the high temperatures and the low temperatures for a given location.

- Provide centimeter graph paper for students to plot and display on a line graph the following temperatures in degrees Fahrenheit for a ten-day period: 78, 74, 76, 80, 85, 78, 88, 90, 92, 95.

Lesson 7-8 (p. 312)

If You Hopped Like a Frog by David M. Schwartz

- This book focuses on comparisons, ratio, proportion, and measurement within entertaining and humorous contexts.

- Have students look at how far a frog can hop in relation to its body length and record that same data for themselves using an agreed-upon unit of measure.

- Have students choose an appropriate graph for displaying the information for each member of the class.

- Look at the information at the back of the book showing how the author calculated the comparisons he used and have groups of students choose another comparison to gather data on and display in an appropriate graph.

Lesson 7-9 (p. 320)

Tiger Math: Learning to Graph from a Baby Tiger
by Ann Whitehead Nagda and Cindy Bickel

- On page 16 of *Tiger Math* there is a double bar graph that compares the weight of T.J. and the weight of Mathew. Read this page, then ask the following questions:

  - How much did T.J weigh at 6 weeks? 10 lbs 10 weeks? 13 lbs

  - How much did Mathew weigh at 6 weeks? 14 lbs 10 weeks? 19 lbs

  - What are we able to do with a double bar graph that we couldn't do with a regular bar graph? Compare two different sets of data.

- On page 24 is a single bar graph. Have the students turn this into a double bar graph by predicting how much meat Mathew would have eaten during those weeks.

8 Develop Fraction Concepts

Lesson 8-1 (p. 333)

Polar Bear Math: Learning about Fractions from Klondike and Snow
by Ann Whitehead Nagda and Cindy Bickel

- Read the story *Polar Bear Math* aloud to the class, and then return to page 24.

- On page 24 there is the recipe for Polar Bear Milk broken into fifths.

  - Just like in the book, ask students to divide

    1 whole batch of milk by $\frac{1}{5}$ using fraction bars.

    They should find out that there are 5 $\frac{1}{5}$s in a batch.

  - To extend the activity ask students to divide

    2 batches of milk into $\frac{1}{5}$s using fraction bars.

Lesson 8-2 (p. 338)

Fractions and Decimals
by Lucille Caron and Philip M. St. Jacques

- Read pages 6–7.

- Review the definitions form proper fraction, improper fraction and mixed number.

- Students are going to play "Who am I?"

- Each student receives two index cards. They need to write either an example of or a riddle about a proper fraction, improper fraction or mixed number. Ex: mixed number — I contain wholes and parts.

- Collect the cards and divide the students into groups.

- Play the game by asking students to solve each card — reward points for correct answers.

Lesson 8-3 (p. 344)

Math Man by Teri Daniels

- Read the story the *Math Man* then use the pumpkin prices found on page 10 to answer the following questions. (It may be helpful to make a class chart of the pounds and prices)

  - Marnie had $3.00 and bought 2 pumpkins. The combined weight of the pumpkins is 7 pounds. The weight difference between the 2 she bought is 1 pound. What 2 pumpkins did he buy?

  - James has 6 coins in his pocket and has exactly enough money to buy a two pound pumpkin. What are the coins in his pocket?

Lesson 8-4 (p. 346)

Fractions and Decimals
by Lucille Caron and Philip M. St. Jacques

- Read pages 6–7.

- Review how to turn a mixed number into an improper fraction.

- Distribute two index cards to each student.

- On one index card, ask students to write a mixed number.

- On the second index card, instruct students that they need to convert the mixed number into an improper fraction. Write the improper fraction on the second card.

- Collect the cards.

- Redistribute two cards to each student.

- Now the students have the task of finding out who has their matches. Ex: Mixed numbers must find their improper fraction.

Lesson 8-5 (p. 350)

Gator Pie by Louise Mathews

- Read the story.

- Ask each student to create a fraction pie.

- Divide the pie for somewhere between 4 and 100 people.

- Tell students that 3 people have eaten slices out of the pie.

- Create a fraction to show this information.

  Ex: $\frac{3}{50}$ — 50 slices cut — 3 colored red to show what has been eaten.

- In groups of five, have students put their fraction pies in order from least to greatest.

- Create a wall display using the fraction pies.

Lesson 8-6 (p. 356)

Fraction Action by Loreen Leedy

- Read the story.

- Introduce the concept of rounding.

- Assign three students to physically be the number line. Give one student the 0 sheet of paper etc.

- Distribute the fraction index cards to each student.

- Ask the students to think about whether their fraction is closest to 0, $\frac{1}{2}$ or 1.

- Have students arrange themselves around the student that is holding the number that they are closest to right now.

- Then repeat the activity asking students to first round their fraction up and switch positions, and then round their fraction down.

CHAPTER 9 Use Factors and Multiples

Lesson 9-1 (p. 373)

Sea Squares by Joy Hulme

- Before reading the book make a set of number cards 0–7 for each child.

- Read and discuss *Sea Squares.* Talk about what a square number is and have them make a list of the square numbers from 0–100.

- Put students in pairs and give each child a set of cards. Put the two sets of cards together and shuffle them. Each child draws two cards and makes a two-digit number. Then the pair makes a list of all the factors for that number. Do the same thing for the other partner's number.

- Compare the factors for each number and decide if there are any factors in common. Circle the ones in common.

Lesson 9-2 (p. 378)

Among the Odds and Evens: A Tale of Adventure by Priscilla Turner

- Read *Among the Odds and Evens* aloud to the class. This is a story about the differences between odd numbers and even numbers and what happens when you add them together.

- Tell the students that today they will learn about another difference between odds and evens. Write the following numbers on the board: 2, 3, 5, 7, 11, 13, and 17, and then ask the following questions:
  - What do all of these numbers have in common? prime
  - Why is 2 the only even numbered prime? All other even numbers are divisible by 2.
  - Name the next prime number after 17. 19

Lesson 9-3 (p. 382)

Fraction Fun by David A. Adler

- Read the story. Introduce the word *equivalent* and its meaning.

- Distribute a fraction to each student, and have him/her draw a pictorial representation of his or her fraction on the back of the index card.

- Tell students that everyone in the class has at least one other equivalent fraction somewhere in the class. (Some people may have more than one).

- Their task is to walk around and find the fraction or fractions that are the equivalent matches to their fraction.

Lesson 9-4 (p. 386)

Give Me Half! by Stuart J. Murphy

- Read the story.

- Introduce the terms *reducing* and *simplest form*.

- Students are now given the task of writing several fractions that all equal $\frac{1}{2}$.

- Ask students to write fractions, that equal $\frac{1}{2}$, for pizzas that have been divided in the following ways. Ex: One pizza in 8 slices $= \frac{4}{8}$.
  1. One pizza divided in 6 slices
  2. One pizza divided in 12 slices
  3. Two pizzas divided into 8 pieces each
  4. Three pizzas divided into 4 pieces each
  5. Three pizzas divided into 6 pieces each
  6. Three pizzas divided into 10 pieces each

Lesson 9-5 (p. 391)

Henry Hikes to Fitchburg by D.B. Johnson

- Before reading, ask students to keep track of the different amounts of money that Henry earns on his trip.

- Read the story.

- Review that change ($) can be written as a fraction with a denominator of 100, and that money less than $1.00 can be written as a decimal.

- Ask students to write each amount of money that Henry earned as both a decimal and a fraction.

  Ex: 88 cents $= \frac{88}{100} = .88$

Literature Support

Lesson 9-6 (p. 394)

Polar Bear Math: Learning About Fractions from Klondike and Snow by Ann Whitehead Nagda and Cindy Bickel

- Read the story *Polar Bear Math* and then complete the activity.

  - Tell the students that in the story we learned a lot of activities Klondike and Snow do for fun, like wrestling, fishing, swimming and eating. Have students create an organized list to determine how many different orders Klondike and Snow can do their activities.

Lesson 9-7 (p. 396)

Marvelous Multiplication: Games and Activities that Make Math Easy and Fun by Lynette Long

- Read pgs. 1–5.

- Review the terms *factor* and *multiple*.

- Tell students that they are going to create a "mad lib" puzzle using multiples. Unlike traditional "mad libs" which use parts of speech, this puzzle will use multiples.

- Each student is to write his/her own story. Ex: Mary went to the store and bought *multiple of 7* bananas.

- The following multiples must be used: multiples of 10, 7, 6, 4, 2, and 11.

- When finished, students swap stories with a neighbor and fill in the multiples in another person's story.

Lesson 9-9 (p. 404)

Fraction Fun by David A. Adler

- Read pages 1–Pizza Math page.

- Tell students that they are going to create "Domino Fractions"

- Give students the first fraction domino of $\frac{8}{12}$. Draw a picture of this fraction as a domino on the board.

- Tell students that they are to create four domino fractions that are less than $\frac{8}{12}$, and two domino fractions that are more than $\frac{8}{12}$.

- Have students draw their dominos in order from least to greatest on a piece of paper.

- Tell students to write the fraction that corresponds with their domino underneath each picture.

CHAPTER 10 Add and Subtract Fractions

Lesson 10-1 (p. 423)

Pizza Counting by Christina Dobson

- Read the story.

- Review the terms *numerator* and *denominator*.

- Use the pizzas in the book to model the fraction toppings. Ex: pg. 4–5 — 10 total toppings — $\frac{1}{10}$ mushrooms, $\frac{3}{10}$ green peppers

- Have students create their own pizzas using the 4 different toppings on pg. 8–9.

- Then instruct the students to write 5 different fraction addition problems and answers to show different combinations of toppings. Ex: mushrooms + green peppers $\frac{1}{10} + \frac{3}{10} = \frac{4}{10}$.

Lesson 10-2 (p. 428)

Gator Pie by Louise Mathews

- Before reading, instruct students to write down all of the fractions that are mentioned in the story.

- Read the story.

- Tell students that they are now going to write their own story about gator pie. In this story, Alvin and Alice have already cut the pie into 100 slices.

- They then meet 5 different people/animals who each eat part of the pie.

- Write the story and show all of the math involved as parts of the pie are eaten.

- Remind students that Alvin and Alice start out with $\frac{100}{100}$ of the pie (one whole).

Lesson 10-3 (p. 434)

How Pizza Came to Queens by Dayal Kaur Khalsa

Materials: index cards

- Read and discuss the story

- Give each student three blank cards and have them write their favorite kind of pizza and one of the following fractions on each card: $\frac{1}{4}$, $\frac{1}{8}$, $\frac{1}{2}$, $\frac{1}{3}$, and $\frac{1}{6}$.

- Mix up the cards and let students take turns drawing cards. They need to build pizzas by converting fractions to like denominators and work to make a whole pizza.

- Once a whole pizza is made, let students draw the pizza they made and display it.

- Have students write a paragraph describing the parts of their pizza. Then have students name their favorite pizza.

Lesson 10-4 (p. 439)

How Pizza Came to Queens by Dayal Kaur Khalsa

Materials: index cards

- Read and discuss the story

- Have students write a sequal to the story.

- The sequal should include a time when the main character subracts fractions with unlike denominators.

- Share your sequals with the class.

Lesson 10-5 (p. 442)

Minnie's Diner by Dayle Ann Dodds

- Place the Following Menu on the Board.

Minnie's Diner	
Soup	$1.25
Salad	.75¢
Sandwich	$2.90
Fries	$1.10
Pie	$3.15

- Read the story *Minnie's Diner*, then tell them that they will be estimating the amount of each boy's check.

- Ask the students to determine if the following are reasonable amounts for each boy's check.
  - Will = $9.00 reasonable
  - Bill = $10.00 not reasonable
  - Phil = $40.00 reasonable
  - Gill = $60.00 not reasonable
  - Dill = $160.00 reasonable

- Now make another table to show how many items would be ordered if instead of doubling the previous order, the next boy would ask for one more of each item.

Lesson 10-6 (p. 444)

Fractions and Decimals by Lucille Caron and Philip M. St Jacques

- Pass out rulers to student groups.

- Write $3\frac{1}{8} + 5\frac{14}{16}$ on the board.

- Help students to identify each mixed number on their rulers and decide what the closest whole number is for each.

- Students should determine that $3 + 6 = 9$.

- Help students to continue finding estimates using their rulers as time permits.

Lesson 10-7 (p. 448)

Fraction Action by Loreen Leedy

- Read pp. 16-21.

- Review that mixed numbers are made up of wholes and parts.

- Tell students that they are going to create a lunch just like the story.

- Give each student an index card with a mixed number on it.

- On the back, students need to draw a food picture of their mixed number.

- Then in groups, students create mixed number addition problems using their food items.

- Have students draw pictures of the problems, write in the mixed numbers, and solve them.

Lesson 10-8 (p. 452)

The Missing Piece by Shel Silverstein

- Read the story.

- Tell students that the character is looking for $\frac{1}{6}$ to fill in its missing piece.

- They are going to write a story about it.

- On his journey, the character meets many mixed numbers. Each time he meets one, he must subtract $\frac{1}{6}$ from the mixed number to figure out what is left. Then each author can decide whether or not the missing piece gets filled.
  Ex: Meets $2\frac{2}{6} - \frac{1}{6} = 2\frac{1}{6}$

- Use the following mixed numbers in the story: $4\frac{3}{6}$, $10\frac{4}{6}$, $6\frac{5}{6}$, $2\frac{1}{6}$, and $7\frac{6}{6}$

Lesson 10-10 (p. 458)

Fractions and Decimals by Lucille Caron and Philip M. St. Jacques

- Read pages 18–19.

- Write the example $4 - \frac{5}{6}$ on the board.

- Create a short word problem about $4 - \frac{5}{6}$. Ex: the group ordered 4 pizzas. $\frac{5}{6}$ of the pizzas were eaten. How much was left over?

- Write the following problems on the board:
  $6 - \frac{4}{9}$, $5 - \frac{2}{3}$, $4 - \frac{1}{7}$, $7 - \frac{2}{10}$.

- In pairs, have the students write a short word problem about each of the subtraction problems on the board.

- Then ask students to solve their problems and show all their work.

- Allow time for class sharing to assess student understanding.

 Use Measures in the Customary System

Lesson 11-1 (p. 477)

Measuring Penny by Loreen Leedy

* Read the story.

* Tell students that they will be focused on measuring length.

* Review standard units of measurement.

* Divide students into groups.

* Have students trace one of the following on their paper:
  * sneaker, foot, hand, hand and arm, (optional) One entire student

* Then have students measure the length of the item and label its length.

* When possible, instruct students to convert inches to feet.

Lesson 11-2 (p. 482)

Zachary Zormer: Shape Transformer
by Joanne Reisberg

* Read the story *Zachary Zormer Shape Transformer* and then have the students make their own expanding frame. The directions for the expanding frame can be found in the story on page 31.

* Before they begin making their frame ask student to measure the perimeter of their index card and then calculate the area. $P = 20$ in., $A = 24$ in.

* When students finish making their expanded frame have them measure its perimeter. (The perimeter and area will not be exact.)

  $P = $ about 45 in.

Lesson 11-3 (p. 484)

Measuring Up! by Sandra Markle

* Read page 29 — "The Beanstalk Caper"

* Write the treasures that Jack found and their weight on the board. (Students can use this as a reference)

* Tell students that a beanstalk has grown outside their classroom, but this beanstalk will hold triple the amount of weight as Jack's.

* Students need to use their own weight and figure out which combinations of treasures can be carried from the giant's castle without "breaking" the beanstalk.

* Tell students to illustrate their findings.

Lesson 11-4 (p. 488)

Millions to Measure by David M. Schwartz

* Read the story.

* Write the chart used to measure volume (ounces, cups, etc) on the board.

* Tell students that they are going to figure out how much juice Hercules, the Huggable Hippo drinks after his workout.

* Here is the problem: If Hercules drinks 5 gallons of juice, how many ounces, cups, pints and quarts does he drink?

* Have students create a colorful picture of Hercules and a chart to show how much juice he drinks.

* Extension: Add a challenge — Figure out how much juice if Hercules drinks $6\frac{1}{2}$ gallons.

Lesson 11-5 (p. 492)

Measuring Penny by Loreen Leedy

- Read the story.

- Focus on Penny's Time Schedule.

- Tell students that they are going to create their own time schedule for a typical Saturday in their life.

- After creating the schedule, have students figure out:

  - How many minutes they are awake from morning until night. Ex: 8 AM − 8 PM = 12 × 60 = 720 minutes.

  - How many hours and minutes that amount is.

  - How many minutes they spend asleep.

  - How many minutes they spend playing during the day.

Lesson 11-7 (p. 500)

Telling Time with Big Mama Cat by Dan Harper

- Read the story *Telling Time with Big Mama Cat.* This story describes all the activities a cat does throughout the day and gives the time of each activity.

- After you read the story ask the following elapsed time questions:

  - At 10:30 Mama Cat woke up from a nap and went outside. She came back inside at 10:45. How long was she outside? 15 min.

  - How much time elapsed from the time Mama Cat ate lunch and then dinner? 6 hours

  - How long was Isabelle at school? 7 hours and 15 minutes

CHAPTER 12 Use Measures in the Metric System

Lesson 12-1 (p. 517)

How Tall How Short How Faraway? by David A. Adler

- Read the story.

- Write the metric system chart from the story on the board and review it.

- Divide students into groups (4 people).

- For this activity, students will be given a time limit to write down as many different things that they can think of that you would measure in meters, kilometers, centimeters, and millimeters. Ex: A road race: kilometers

- Students will need four pieces of paper. Each page should have a different measurement heading.

- When time is up, allow students time to share their lists and provide correction as needed.

Lesson 12-2 (p. 522)

Minnie's Diner by Dayle Ann Dodds

- Place the Following Menu on the Board.

Minnie's Diner	
Soup	$1.25
Salad	.75¢
Sandwich	$2.90
Fries	$1.10
Pie	$3.15

- Read the story *Minnie's Diner.*

- Have students put together 3 different meals. Each meal must be under $5.

- Students should share the meals they put together to determine if they are reasonable.

Lesson 12-3 (p. 524)

Measure with Metric by Franklyn M. Branley

- Read the story.

- Write the measures for mass on the board.

- Discuss a few examples of things that you would measure in grams or kilograms. Allow a few minutes for group brainstorming.

- Let students know that grams can be compared to ounces and kilograms to pounds. Ex: Measure a dog in kilograms.

- In groups, have students use magazine pictures to create two collages — one for grams and one for kilograms.

- Display the collages in the classroom.

Lesson 12-4 (p. 527)

Millions to Measure by David M. Schwartz

Materials: 2 colors of index cards

- Read the story.

- Focus on the use of liters and milliliters to measure water after the race. What does the prefix milli- mean?

- If the dog drinks 2 liters of water, how can we find out how many milliliters he drank? Discuss.

- Give students 2 colors of index cards, 1 color for liters and the other for milliliters. Instruct each student to make 5 liter cards and 5 milliliter cards. Write a number on the liter card. Write the matching amount of milliliters on a milliliter card.

- In groups of 3, play Metric Matching. To play lay all cards face down. The first player turns 1 of each color over. If they match the player keeps them and goes again. If they do not match, turn them over and it's the next players turn.

Lesson 12-5 (p. 533)

Mathematics by Irving Adler

- Read page 16.

- Have students work in pairs.

- Distribute an amount of play money to each pair.

- Explain that in business, that a gain shows + and a loss shows −

- Each pair counts their money and writes down the amount.

- Give students commands with losses/gains. Each pair keeps track of their losses/gains on a sheet of paper. Students share totals at the end. Ex: You gained $20.00, but spent $45.00. Students would write +20, −45

- Because each pair was given a different amount of money, each pair will have a different ending total.

Lesson 12-6 (p. 537)

Measuring Up! by Sandra Markle

- Read pg. 31

- Provide students with directions on how to create a thermometer with both Farenheit and Celsius — use book as a model.

- After students create their thermometers, divide them into groups and distribute newspapers to each group.

- Select 5–10 cities either nationally or globally or both.

- Students need to:
  1. Figure out today's temperature in both Farenheit and Celsius.
  2. Label each thermometer with the city and its temperatures.

CHAPTER 13 Identify, Compare, and Classify Geometric Figures

Lesson 13-1 (p. 557)

Shape Up! by David A. Adler

- This book illustrates parallel and perpendicular lines with stick pretzels, squares, and other polygons.

- Have students use an index card to draw and cut a 2-inch square and a hexagon with 1-inch sides. Number all sides of the figures.

- Have students place their shapes on lined notebook paper and determine which sides of each figure are parallel, which intersect, and which intersect perpendicularly in each figure by extending each side. The square has parallel sides that intersect perpendicularly at the vertices; the hexagon has parallel sides but no sides that intersect perpendicularly.

- Try an octagon!

Lesson 13-2 (p. 562)

Circus Caps for Sale by Esphyr Slobodkina

- Read about the peddler with different colored caps stacked on his head.

- Explain to students that using logic will help them answer this question: in how many different arrangements could the peddler stack the colored caps on his head if he had one each of the gray cap, the brown cap, and the red cap? 6 How many if there were 4 different-colored caps? 12

- This is a combinations problem that requires a logical approach and systematic ordering. Suggest students draw pictures, use counters or letters to represent the caps, or construct an organized list.

Lesson 13-3 (p. 566)

Square Triangle Round Skinny by Vladimir Radunsky

- This is set of board books illustrating each concept in the title with a variety of real world examples.

- Have students design a single triangle book with these attributes: right, acute, obtuse, equilateral, isosceles, and scalene.

- They need to illustrate their book and try to find several examples of these triangle types in the environment of the classroom, school, home, or town/city.

- After all students have finished their book have a sharing session.

- The author used the attribute "skinny", ask students if they think any of their examples are "skinny", narrow, slim or small.

Lesson 13-4 (p. 570)

Zachary Zormer Shape Transformer by Joanne Reisberg

- "Something fun to measure" is an activity each week in Zack's classroom. He makes a Moebius strip and an expanding frame. (Directions are given at the end of the book.)

- Then he shines a flashlight on a piece of notebook paper showing the beam can illuminate from 1 square inch to the whole page.

- Have students use an $8\frac{1}{2} \times 11$-inch piece of paper to calculate: perimeter, area, and the sum of the 4 angles. perimeter = 38 in.; area = 93.5 square inches; sum of angles = 360 degrees Repeat with different quadrilaterals.

Literature Support

Lesson 13-6 (p. 578)

Geometry by Lucille Caron and Philip M. St. Jacques

Materials: grid paper

- Read pp. 38–39. Have students follow along with what is read on grid paper. Draw how the picture slides in different directions, not changing the size or shape of the object. Let students know this is a *translation.*

- Tell students they will have a chance to practice translating an *image* on a grid. Discuss the term.

- Tell students to number their grid along the *x* and *y* axis. Instruct students to make a shape with 4 vertices.

- Have students translate their shape 3 spaces to the right. All of their vertices should line up with the original.

- Allow students to translate their shape one more time in the direction of their choice. Identify strategies students used to translate their image.

Lesson 13-7 (p. 582)

Round Trip by Ann Jonas

- Before reading, introduce the terms symmetry and reflection.

- Read the story.

- Ask students to draw a coordinate grid on their paper.

- Students can work in groups, but each student should create their own piece.

- Distribute pattern blocks.

- Students will use the pattern blocks to create a design in one quadrant and trace in the pattern.

- Then, they swap papers with a neighbor, and the other person must create a reflection of the first pattern and trace it in a different quadrant of the coordinate grid.

Lesson 13-8 (p. 586)

Geometry by Lucille Caron and Philip M. St. Jacques

- Read pages 42–43.

- Divide students into groups.

- In a small space on the paper, each student draws his/her own shape. Ask students to include a detail in the shape (show example from book).

- They then pass the paper to the right, and the new group member must draw the shape rotated 90 degrees to the right.

- The activity is repeated until each member of the group has drawn each shape rotated.

- When finished, each group member should have four rotated shapes on his/her paper.

Lesson 13-9 (p. 591)

Geometry by Lucille Caron and Philip M. St. Jacques

- Read pages 42–43.

- Define *slide, flip,* and *turn.*

- Divide students into groups of three.

- Distribute an index card with pattern to each group.

- Each member of the group must take the given pattern and create either a slide, flip or turn of the pattern on the card.

- Students exchange cards within the group, and create a new slide, flip or turn of a different pattern.

- Continue the activity, until each member of the group has created a slide, a flip and a turn for the pattern cards in the group.

14 Measure Perimeter, Area, and Volume

Lesson 14-1 (p. 608)

Geometry by Lucille Caron and Philip M. St. Jacques

- Read pgs 46–47.

- Students will create a code and a shape puzzle.

- The alphabet letters of the code are going to equal the measurements of different perimeters. Ex: The letter A = 10 units. Any time a student wants to use the letter A in his/her code, they must draw a shape that has a perimeter of 10 units.

- Each student begins by creating his/her own code.

- Then the student selects a word, and creates the puzzle by drawing different shapes with perimeters that match the code.

- Students then solve each other's puzzles.

Lesson 14-2 (p. 612)

Sir Circumference and the Sword in the Cone
by Cindy Neuschwander

- This story is a fantasy where five knights compete to find a specific shape from geometric nets of three-dimensional shapes. The winner who finds a sword in a specific cone using clues of given dimensions becomes heir to the throne.

- On p. 12 a chart shows an equilateral rectangular prism called a cube and a rectangular prism.

- Have students look at the nets on p. 5 to construct a cube and a rectangular prism using inch grid paper. Have them find the area of each of their prisms using the grid paper and multiplication.

Lesson 14-3 (p. 616)

Sir Cumference and the Isle of Immeter
by Cindy Neuschwander

Materials: grid paper

- After reading the story, discuss the game of "inners and outers."

- How are they finding the outers? How are they finding the inner squares?

- Identify "inners" as area and "outers" as perimeter. Discuss strategies used to find the area and perimeter.

- Give students grid paper. Students will challenge a partner to identify the "inners" of 3 shapes. Have students draw 3 rectangular or square shapes. Tell them to find the area of each and list it on a separate paper. Exchange with another student; determine the area of each shape. Students should return papers and check areas their partner calculated.

Lesson 14-4 (p. 624)

Sir Cumference and the Sword in the Cone
by Cindy Neuschwander

- Before reading, write the lesson vocabulary on the board.

- Read the story.

- Divide the class into groups, and distribute one geo solid to each group

- Explain to the students that like Sir Cumference, that they will be writing a riddle about their solid. An example for a sphere: I do not have any edges.

- The riddle needs to include: a net (use ones in story or textbook), and information on the bases, vertices, edges and faces.

Extension: Once groups have completed their riddles, they can give their riddle to another group to solve.

Lesson 14-5 (p. 628)

How Tall How Short How Faraway?
by David A. Adler

- After you read through the book have students look closely at the description of the more than 300 year-old metric system of measurement.

- Have partners work together to trace their hand spans and measure them in centimeters.

- Ask if their hand spans are more or less than a decimeter. (A decimeter is $\frac{1}{10}$ of a meter = 10 centimeters.)

- Have students use their hand spans to measure the length or width of the classroom and determine if the linear measurement is more than or less than 10 meters, a dekameter.

Lesson 14-6 (p. 631)

Geometry by Lucille Caron and Philip M. St. Jacques

- Read pgs. 58–59.

- Review area = $\ell \times w$, and volume = area of base $\times$ h

- Divide students into pairs

- This activity involves some problem solving. Assign students the measurements for the area of a base and height of a figure.

- Using the area of the base, students need to figure out a possible length and width. (There are many possibilities).

- Then students draw the rectangular prism using the length, width and height.

- Finally, students calculate the volume.

Lesson 14-7 (p. 640)

Sir Circumference and the Sword in the Cone
by Cindy Neuschwander

Materials: inch grid paper

- This story is a fantasy where five knights compete to find a specific shape from geometric nets of three-dimensional shapes. The winner who finds a sword in a specific cone using clues of given dimensions becomes heir to the throne.

- On p. 12, a chart shows an equilateral rectangular prism called a cube and a rectangular prism.

- Have students look at the nets on p. 5 to construct a cube and a rectangular prism using inch grid paper. Have them find the area of each of their prisms using the grid paper and multiplication.

Lesson 14-8

Sir Cumference and the Sword in the Cone by Cindy Neuschwander

- Read the story.

- On p.11, have students focus on the 3 dimensional shapes. Ask, what can we measure? If it is the shape that fits in the palm of his hands, what measurement would you use? How would you determine area? perimeter? Write formulas on the board.

- On p.16, how would you find the volume of what could fit in the castle courtyard? Write formula on the board.

- Have students work with a partner to write 3 problems for Sir Cumference to solve based on the story. Write 1 problem each for area, perimeter, and volume.

- Tell students to exchange word problems with another group and try to solve their problems. Discuss how each group decided what formula they would need to use.

CHAPTER 15 Use Probability to Make Predictions

Lesson 15-1 (p. 661)

Do You Wanna Bet? by Jean Cushman

- Introduce the term *probability*.

- Read pages 1–15 to the students.

- After reading, introduce the vocabulary and refer back to the story for examples of each.

- Divide students into 5 groups. Tell each group privately whether they are: the certain group, the impossible group, the equally likely group, more likely group, or the less likely group.

- Each group must write 3 statements that give a clue as to which group they are. Ex: Impossible — We all ate worms for breakfast.

- Students share their statements, and others must guess which group is which.

Lesson 15-2 (p. 668)

Do You Wanna Bet? by Jean Cushman

- Begin reading on pg. 20 with "Probability is determined by dividing …"

- Write the fraction for determining probability on the board.

- Divide the students into groups.

- There are several parts to the activity.

   1. Students cut out 5 different shapes. They may choose triangles, circles or squares in different colors. Combine all shapes in the group.

   2. Students write 5 probability questions. Ex: What is the probability of having a red triangle?

   3. Students then pass all of their shapes and questions to another group. Remind students to write their answers in fraction form.

Lesson 15-3 (p. 674)

Polar Bear Math: Learning about Fractions from Klondike and Snow
by Ann Whitehead Nagda and Cindy Bickel

- Read the story *Polar Bear Math* and then complete the activity.

   - Tell the students that in the story we learned a lot of activities Klondike and Snow do for fun, like wrestling, fishing, swimming and eating. Have students create an organized list to determine how many different orders Klondike and Snow can do their activities.

Lesson 15-4 (p. 677)

Odds and Chances for Kids by Manfred G. Riedel

- Read pages 3–13 aloud to students.

- Tell students to pretend that they are going on a field trip to a camp. At this camp, there are many different activities that they can choose to participate in. Students can choose two activities, and the staff wants the students to figure out all of the activity combinations before they arrive.

- Write activity choices on the board: ropes course, hiking, mountain biking, fishing, bird watching, swimming and canoeing.

- Tell students to use tree diagrams to show their work.

Literature Bibliography

CHAPTER 1 Use Place Value

Alexander, Who Used to Be Rich Last Sunday by Judy Viorst. Simon & Schuster Children's Publishing Co. 1978.

How Much Is a Million? by David M. Schwartz. William Morrow and Company, Inc. 1985.

Little Numbers and Pictures that Show Just How Little They Are! by Edward Packard. Millbrook Press, Inc. 2001.

Math Man by Teri Daniels. Scholastic, Inc. 2001.

One Riddle One Answer by Lauren Thompson. Scholastic, Inc. 2001.

CHAPTER 2 Add and Subtract Whole Numbers and Decimals

Coyotes All Around by Stuart J. Murphy. Harper Collins Children's Books. 2000.

Math Man by Teri Daniels. Scholastic, Inc. 2001.

Pigs Will Be Pigs by Amy Axelrod. Simon & Schuster Children's Publishing Co. 1994.

Rajah's Rice, The by David Barry. David Barry. 1994.

Sold! A Mathematics Tale by Nathan Zimelman. Charlesbridge Publishing, Inc. 1994.

Spaghetti and Meatballs for All by Marilyn Burns. Scholastic, Inc. 1996.

CHAPTER 3 Multiply Whole Numbers

Amanda Bean's Amazing Dream by Cindy Neuschwander. Scholastic, Inc. 1998.

Baby Oaks from Math for All Seasons by Greg Tang. Scholastic, Inc. 2002.

Beanstalk The Measure of a Giant by Ann McCallum.

Minnie's Diner by Dayle Ann Dodds. Candlewick Press. 2004.

My Full Moon is Square by Elinor J. Pinczes. Houghton Mifflin Company. 2002.

Perfect Ten from The Best of Times by Greg Tang. Scholastic, Inc. 2001.

Pigs Will Be Pigs by Amy Axelrod. Simon & Schuster Children's Publishing Co. 1994.

Sea Squares by Joy N. Hulme. Hyperion Books for Children. 1991.

Literature Support

CHAPTER 4 Divide Whole Numbers

17 Kings and 42 Elephants by Margaret Mahy. Penguin Books USA, Inc. 1972.

Betcha! by Stuart J. Murphy. Harper Collins Children's Books. 1997.

Cut Down to Size at High Noon by Scott Sundby. Charlesbridge Publishing, Inc. 2000.

If You Hopped Like a Frog by David M. Schwartz. Scholastic, Inc. 1999.

Pigs Will Be Pigs by Amy Axelrod. Simon & Schuster Children's Publishing Co. 1994.

Place for Zero, A by Angeline Sparagna LoPresti. Charlesbridge Publishing, Inc. 2003.

Remainder of One by Elinor J. Pinczes. Houghton Mifflin Company. 1995.

 CHAPTER 5 Use Algebraic Expressions

Amanda Bean's Amazing Dream by Cindy Neuschwander. Scholastic, Inc. 1998.

If You Made a Million by David M. Schwartz.

Librarian Who Measured the Earth, The by Kathryn Lasky. Little Brown & Company. 1994.

Once Upon a Dime by Nancy Kelly Allen. Charlesbridge Publishing, Inc. 1999.

Pizza Counting by Christina Dobson. Charlesbridge Publishing, Inc. 2003.

Two of Everything by Lily Toy Hong. Albert Whitman & Company. 1993.

 CHAPTER 6 Use Equations and Function Tables

Fly on the Ceiling A Math Myth, The by Dr. Julie Glass. Random House Company.

Hottest Coldest Highest Deepest by Steve Jenkins.

How Do You Know What Time It Is? by Robert E. Wells. Albert Whitman & Company. 2002.

Place for Zero: A Math Adventure, A by Angeline Sparagna LoPresti. Charlesbridge Publishing, Inc. 2003.

Sir Cumference and the Sword in the Cone by Cindy Neuschwander. Charlesbridge Publishing, Inc. 2003.

Warlord's Puzzle, The by Walton Pilegard. Pelican Publishing Company, Inc. 2000.

 CHAPTER 7 Display and Interpret Data

Counting Jennie by Helena Clare Pittman. Penguin Books USA, Inc. 1994.

G is for Googol by David Schwartz. Tricycle Press. 1998.

If You Hopped Like a Frog by David M. Schwartz. Scholastic, Inc. 1999.

Tiger Math by Ann Whitehead Nagda and Bickel. Henry Holt and Company, LLC. 1997.

Tree in the Forest, A by Jan Thornhill. Simon & Schuster Children's Publishing Co. 1991.

Weather by Seymour Simon. Harper Collins Children's Books. 1993.

Zooming and Creeping by Barbara Taylor. Peter Bedrick. 2001.

Literature Bibliography

CHAPTER 8 — Develop Fraction Concepts

Fraction Action by Loreen Leedy. Holiday House. 1994.

Fractions and Decimals by Lucille Caron and Philip M. St. Jacques.

Gator Pie by Louise Mathews. Sundance Publishing. 1979.

Math Man by Teri Daniels. Scholastic, Inc. 2001.

Polar Bear Math by Ann Whitehead. Henry Holt and Company, LLC. 2004.

CHAPTER 9 — Use Factors and Multiples

Among the Odds and Evens by Priscilla Turner. Farrar, Straus, and Giroux Inc. 1999.

Fraction Fun by David A. Adler. Holiday House. 1996.

Give Me Half! by Stuart J. Murphy. Harper Collins Children's Books.

Henry Hikes to Fitchburg by D.B. Johnson. Houghton Mifflin Company. 2000.

Marvelous Multiplication by Lynette Long. John Wiley & Sons Inc. 2000.

Polar Bear Math by Ann Whitehead. Henry Holt and Company, LLC. 2004.

Sea Squares by Joy N. Hulme. Harper Collins Children's Books. 1997.

CHAPTER 10 — Model Adding and Subtracting Fractions

Fraction Action by Loreen Leedy. Holiday House. 1994.

Fractions and Decimals by Lucille Caron and Philip M. St. Jacques. Enslow Publishers Inc. 2000.

Gator Pie by Louise Mathews. Sundance Publishing. 1979.

How Pizza Came to Queens by Dayal Kaur Khalsa. Crown Publishers, 1989.

Let's Investigate Estimating by Marion Smoothy.

Minnie's Diner by Dayle Ann Dodds. Candlewick Press. 2004.

Missing Piece, The by Shel Silverstein.

Pizza Counting by Christina Dobson.

CHAPTER 11 — Use Measures in the Customary System

Measuring Penny by Loreen Leedy. Henry Holt and Company, LLC. 1997.

Measuring Penny by Loreen Leedy. Holiday House. 1997.

Measuring Up! by Sandra Markle. Atheneum/Richard Jackson Books. 1995.

Millions to Measure by David M. Schwartz. Harper Collins Children's Books. 1998.

Telling Time with Big Mama Cat by Dan Harper. Harcourt Brace & Company. 1998.

Zachery Zormer Shape Transformer by Joanne Reisberg. Charlesbridge Publishing, Inc. 2006.

CHAPTER 12 Use Measures in the Metric System

How Tall, How Short, How Far Away by David A. Adler. Holiday House. 2000.

Mathematics by Irving Adler. Golden Press. 1977.

Measure with Metric by Franklyn M. Branley.

Measuring Up! by Sandra Markle. Atheneum/Richard Jackson Books. 1995.

Millions to Measure by David M. Schwartz. Harper Collins Children's Books. 1998.

Minnie's Diner by Dayle Ann Dodds.

CHAPTER 13 Identify, Compare, and Classify Geometric Figures

Circus Caps for Sale by Esphyr Slobodkina. Harper Collins Children's Books. 1967.

Geometry by Lucille Caron and Phillip M. St. Jacques.

Round Trip by Ann Jonas. Harper Collins Children's Books. 1983.

Shape Up! by David A. Adler. Holiday House. 1998.

Square Triangle Round Skinny by Vladimir Radunsky.

Zachery Zormer Shape Transformer by Joanne Reisberg.

CHAPTER 14 Measure Perimeter, Area, and Volume

Geometry by Lucille Caron and Philip M. St. Jacques. Enslow Publishers Inc. 2001.

How Tall, How Short, How Far Away by David A. Adler. Holiday House. 2000.

Sir Cumference and the Isle of Inmeter by Cindy Neuschwander. Charlesbridge Publishing, Inc. 2006.

Sir Cumference and the Sword in the Cone by Cindy Neuschwander. Charlesbridge Publishing, Inc. 2006.

Sir Cumference and the Sword in the Cone by Cindy Neuschwander. Charlesbridge Publishing, Inc. 2003.

CHAPTER 15 Use Probability to Make Predictions

Do You Wanna Bet? by Jean Cushman. Houghton Mifflin Company. 1991.

Odds and Chances for Kids by Manfred G. Riedel. Pearson Educ. Permissions Dept. 1979.

Polar Bear Math by Ann Whitehead. Henry Holt and Company, LLC. 2004.

Professional Development

So You're Teaching Fifth Grade...
An Introduction to the Social, Physical, and Cognitive Development of Fifth Graders

Fifth grade is a time of change for many children, both physically and socially. Many are entering adolescence, and those who are not are often aware that others are changing. Academically, fifth graders are beginning to encounter the more abstract thinking required in connecting symbols to problem solving situations and connecting formulas to concepts such as perimeter, area, and volume. As a fifth grade teacher, you are an important influence as children enter this critical grade level where passing standardized tests is a promotion requirement in mathematics and reading.

Physical and Social Development

Probably the most important thing you should keep in mind about fifth graders' physical development is hormonal changes. Some of the girls are already going through hormonal changes that sometimes cause emotional outbursts and negative attitudes. Some of the boys are "discovering" girls for the first time. Overall, they are very active and energetic, but they can become uncooperative because they think that they do not require supervision. With such a mix of emotions and hormones, many students can become discipline problems.

However, most fifth graders are still like primary students who yearn for praise and recognition. They respond to all kinds of positive reinforcement, including stickers, points, coupons, homework passes, or just words of praise. Because this age group yearns for social acceptance and achievement, they work successfully in cooperative groups in a structured environment.

Early in the year, students might not be developmentally ready for the abstract thinking that most algorithms and mathematics procedures require. They are generally more successful in their learning when they are able to explore first with concrete materials, make a transition to a pictorial representation, and then connect the learning to the symbolic representation. Students need to make sense of their learning through manipulatives, such as base-10 blocks, decimal squares, fraction bars, and geoboards. They even look forward to communicating the mathematics they learn by logging in their math journals.

What Fifth Graders Should Know

As you prepare to teach your students mathematics this year, there are some major expectations and foundational skills to consider. Entering fifth grade, the students should understand large numbers and be able to add, subtract, multiply, and divide whole numbers in meaningful problem situations. They should be able to compare fractions and relate decimals to fractions that name tenths and hundredths using concrete objects and pictorial models. And they should be able to concretely and pictorially add and subtract decimals to the hundredths. They also should come with experiences in describing and identifying two-and three-dimensional figures using formal geometric vocabulary terms. They have learned to measure to solve problems including perimeter and area, but they have only learned to find volume concretely.

It is highly recommended that at the beginning of grade five, students are assessed on the core content of the lower grades including basic facts recall, estimation, place value, geometric vocabulary, and algorithms for all whole number operations. This type of diagnostic assessment will be your guideline as you provide for daily recursive review in problematic skills and concepts to reach higher levels of proficiency and fluency.

Abstract Representations in 5th Grade

A major shift in instruction begins in fifth grade where students are now expected to move from concrete experiences and pictorial representations to abstract symbolic representations. They are now expected to follow abstract procedures such as finding a common denominator to compare fractions or find equivalent fractions instead of only using concrete models such as fraction bars. In decimals, they shift from adding and subtracting decimals with decimal squares to using the abstract algorithm. They now compare and order fractions abstractly without the use of decimal models. In algebraic thinking, they are now using formal equations including variables to represent problem solving situations. And in measurement, the students shift to connecting models for perimeter, area, and volume with their respective formulas. It is important that the students are not rushed into rules or procedures in any of these concepts before they are developmentally ready. In comparing fractions, for example, the students should first develop their number sense skills to help them use benchmarks such as $\frac{1}{2}$ to compare fractions before being required to find a common denominator without understanding. The students can make the bridge to abstract representations, but they need concrete and meaningful experiences first to make sense of the mathematics.

Concepts New to Fifth Grade
Fifth grade is the first year in which students are introduced to identifying common factors of a set of whole numbers; identifying prime and composite numbers; adding and subtracting fractions with like denominators; locating and naming points on a coordinate grid; describing, predicting results, and listing all possible outcomes of probability experiments; making line graphs; and describing data on tables or graphs using terms such as median, mode, and range. To develop conceptual understanding, it is essential that these concepts are taught concretely by having students drawing rectangles to identify prime numbers and composite numbers or by having the students create a life-sized coordinate grid to model ordered pairs. The students should use concrete objects and pictorial representations to model addition and subtraction of fractions. They should use estimation and informal

Considerations for Grade 5
Important mathematical skills and concepts for students in grade five to acquire are as follows:

- Identifying common factors.
- Identifying prime and composite numbers.
- Adding and subtracting fractions with unlike denominators.
- Locating and naming points on a coordinate grid.
- Describing and predicting results of probability experiments.
- Describing data presented in tables and graphs using median, mode, and range.
- Making line graphs.

methods and benchmarks to develop computation of fractions instead of just being told to add the numerators when the denominators are the same. The students need to develop a strong understanding of simple computations of fractions so they will have the foundation needed for adding and subtracting fractions with unlike denominators in sixth grade.

Success Throughout the Year
Once each of these new concepts are taught and assessed, the students should still be provided with on-going recursive review to provide for long term retention. "Mathematical concepts that students are in the process of constructing are formulated little by little over time" (Van De Walle, 2007). As you progress through the year, make sure you provide for daily interactive recursive review of problematic concepts such as prime and composite numbers, common factors, comparing fractions, finding equivalent fractions, comparing and ordering decimals, transformations, and other geometric vocabulary. Make sure that your instruction is intellectually stimulating for your active students by presenting your daily lessons in an engaging problem solving context. Allow your students to communicate mathematically as they justify their solutions using different problem solving strategies. Allow them to develop their number sense

skills as they use estimation to determine reasonable results. But most of all, learn to let go and learn from your students. Be a facilitator of instruction, and you will see your students develop into mathematically proficient learners!

References
Elementary and Middle School Mathematics, Teaching Developmentally, 6th Ed. John Van De Walle, Pearson Education, Inc.

Mary Esther Reynosa has been an educator in Texas for 27 years. She is currently the Instructional Specialist for Elementary Mathematics in Northside ISD in San Antonio. She has served as a district mathematics leader in San Antonio for 10 years and has been a classroom teacher for intermediate grades for 16 years in Edgewood ISD and Plano ISD. Her education includes a Bachelor of Arts in English and Master of Arts in Education and Educational Administration.

Reaching All Learners: Providing Equity in Mathematics Education

Reaching All Learners makes mathematics understanding and mastery obtainable to all students, and supports teachers and parents as they help students attain that mastery. The goal of Reaching All Learners is to provide every person with ample and equitable opportunities to approach mathematics. When mathematics educators discuss equity in mathematics teaching and learning, their language often includes phrases that include all children, such as "mathematics for all children" or "mathematics opportunity for every child." Inherent in this language is the desire to provide every child high quality mathematics education that will give them access to professions and careers of their choice (Malloy, 2004).

Equity in mathematics education is about access—that is, Reaching All Learners. However, we have not been successful at achieving measurable equity in achievement, which means that students do not have the opportunity to acquire skills necessary to access 70% of careers of today (Moses, 2001). Schoenfeld discusses the

" Reaching All Learners calls for reasonable and appropriate accommodations to be made to promote access and attainment for all students."

"potential for providing high quality mathematics instruction for all students" (p. 13) from a systemic perspective. He lays out four systemic conditions that are necessary for achieving this goal: "(a) high quality curriculum; (b) stable, knowledgeable, and professional teaching community; (c) high quality assessment that is aligned with curricular goals; (d) and stability and mechanisms for the evolution of curricula, assessment, and professional development" (Schoenfeld, 2002). These conditions are critical for schools and districts to consider and implement as they progress toward the ultimate goal: ample and equitable opportunities in mathematics.

It Begins With Teachers

Teachers often seek help by going to conferences and attending professional development sessions where they see many activities and investigations that augment the presentation of varied topics, but many teachers do not know how to fully create an effective and equitable classroom culture that offers learning opportunities for all students.

In order for students to have equal access mathematics, teachers must have strong math backgrounds and instructional skills. They have to be confident in teaching mathematics, and they must have *access* to ongoing staff development that is available when it is needed. Because teachers and students have varied styles of teaching and learning, it is important to recognize that there is no "one" correct way to teach mathematics. Teachers, more than any other single factor, influence what mathematics students learn and if they master the material.

Flexible Instruction

As students are expected to learn at higher levels and to attain higher standards in mathematics, educators must provide all students with the opportunity and support to achieve these higher goals. Reaching All Learners ensures that the needs of each student are addressed in a manner that allows students to use their own personal strengths to attain the goals expected of them. Reaching All Learners does not mean that every student receives the same instruction; rather, it calls for reasonable and appropriate accommodations to be made to promote access and attainment for all students.

Reaching All Learners provides a two-pronged approach to reaching all learners in the classroom. Reaching All Learners addresses the different learning styles all students bring to the learning process. Reaching All Learners addresses the needs of special student populations, including students of different learning abilities, gifted students, IEP students, and speakers of different languages. Teachers must be able to *differentiate* instruction for students of varied learning styles, prior experiences, interests, socialization needs, and comfort zones (Benjamin, 2005) and abilities.

Getting Parents Involved

Emphasizing parental involvement at home in math learning is another aspect of Reaching All Learners. Research has shown that the more parents are involved with their children's learning, the more successful children are in school (U.S. Department of Education, 1994). Reaching All Learners can help parents understand the skills and procedures used by their children in mathematics learning. To ensure Reaching All Learners, activities that are easy to follow and use everyday materials, are an ideal bridge between the classroom and home environments. Such materials must be informative, useful, and easy for parents to use.

Reaching All Learners: A Two-Pronged Approach

- Reaching All Learners addresses the different learning styles all students bring to the learning process.
- Reaching All Learners addresses the needs of special student populations, including students of different learning abilities, gifted students, IEP students, and speakers of different languages.

Reaching All Learners helps to guide parents in their efforts with their children, making them more productive (Epstein, 1994). Reaching All Learners is designed to help students attain mathematical standards, help teachers gain a broader understanding of mathematics, and help parents support their children at home. If all students, teachers, and parents are to be involved in mathematics, a mathematics program must be equitable and accessible.

Making Reaching All Learners Work

Equity is a key aspect of learning and understanding. *All* students can learn math, *all* teachers can successfully teach math, and *all* parents can support math learning at home—the key is to make mathematics *accessible to all.*

References

Benjamin, A. *Differentiated instruction using technology.* Larchmont, NY: Eye on Education, 2005.

Epstein, Joyce L. "Theory to Practice: School and Family Partnerships Lead to School Improvement," in *School, Family, and Community Interaction: A View from the Firing Lines*, edited by Cheryl L. Fagnano and Beverly Z. Werver, Boulder, CO: Westview Press, 1994. 32–52.

Malloy, C. E. "Equity in mathematics education is about access." Eds. R. Rubenstein and G. Bright. *2004 NCTM Yearbook: Effective mathematics teaching.* Reston, VA: NCTM, 2004. 1–14.

Moses, R. P., & Cobb, Jr., C. E. *Radical equations: Math literacy and civil rights.* Boston: Beacon Press, 2001.

Schoenfeld, A. "Making mathematics work for all children: Issues of standards, testing, and equity." *Educational Research*, 31. 2002. 13–25.

U.S. Department of Education. *Goals 2000: A World-Class Education for Every Child.* Washington D.C.: U.S. Government Printing Office, 1994.

Carol E. Malloy is Associate Professor in Mathematics Education in the School of Education at the University of North Carolina at Chapel Hill. She teaches secondary mathematics methods courses, mathematics courses for middle and elementary pre-service students, and graduate courses in curriculum and foundations. Carol was a member of the NCTM Board of Directors 1998–2002, NCTM Standards 2000 writing team, and president of the Benjamin Banneker Association. She has 20 years teaching experience in public schools across the United States.

Professional Development

English Learners and Mathematics: Best Practices for Effective Instruction

Anecdotal information from classroom teachers as well as evidence from research has demonstrated that the trend toward using more language in mathematics has seriously affected the achievement of students whose first language is not English. In response to this, the National Council of Teachers of Mathematics (NCTM) emphasizes communication "as an essential part of mathematics and mathematics education" and that "second-language learners in particular need to have opportunities and be given encouragement and support for speaking, writing, reading and listening in mathematics classes." Such efforts have the potential to help second-language learners overcome barriers that will facilitate "communicating to learn mathematics and learning to communicate mathematically" (NCTM, 2000).

Research done on effective mathematics instruction for English Learners (ELs) has identified the following best practices. These can be categorized as cultural, instructional and linguistic.

Cultural Considerations

Be aware of how children's home cultures and previous experiences can contribute to their mathematics learning (Gonzalez, et al., 1995; Tikunoff, 1985). ELs bring rich, although often different, experiences with them into the classroom. Consult with bilingual staff and other cultural brokers to find out what

those experiences may be. Then use your students' prior knowledge to create contexts for instruction that are meaningful to them (Garrison & Mora, 1999). This is especially important when students are asked to solve word problems, for in order to do so, they need to be able to picture and understand the situation. This is extremely difficult to do if their experiences do not allow them to visualize what the problem is about.

"ELs bring rich, although often different, experiences with them into the classroom. Consult with bilingual staff and other cultural brokers to find out what those experiences may be."

Instructional Considerations

Teaching the concept before the math can help ELLs conceptualize what they are learning without having to master the language first (Khisty

& Viego, 1999). This can be through the use of pictures, video, manipulatives, realia (actual objects instead of just pictures or models), games, and graphic organizers (Krashen, 1981; Garrison & Mora, 1999). In addition to using these kinesthetic and visual/spatial approaches to teaching concepts, it is important to also encourage students to learn from each other. Working out problems with the aid of peers instead of individually supports the learning styles of many students who come from cultures in which collaborative learning is the norm rather than the exception.

Linguistic Considerations

If teachers structure classroom activities so that students have to speak and write about mathematics, there will be multiple opportunities to use the language of mathematics (Gee, 1992). This is best done if the teacher engages students in instructional conversations that include the use of questions (Khisty & Viego, 1999),

Vocabulary Word	Common Meaning	Mathematical Meaning
table	piece of furniture often used for eating	visual representation of data
foot	appendage at the end of one's leg	standard unit of measurement equal to 12 inches
problem	situation that is difficult to resolve	math exercise

collaboration and group work (Garrison & Mora, 1999). It is also important that while talking about mathematics students be encouraged to use the technical language associated with it once the concept is learned – for example, using "minus" instead of "take away" and including terms such as quotient, dividend, and divisor.

Other vocabulary that needs to be explicitly addressed are terms that can have both mathematical and common meanings. A table can be a piece of furniture, but in mathematics it often refers to a visual representation of data. Round, square, foot, and problem are other examples of such terms. As you are planning lessons, note these words and make sure that ELs understand that the common meaning is different than the technical.

In addition to vocabulary there are numerous other language features that can be problematic for ELs in the mathematics classroom. Seek out the language experts at your school, bilingual teachers and aides and teachers of English as a second language, to collaborate about how these challenges can be addressed.

Unique Needs

In order to ensure that all students achieve to their potential, Reaching All Learners stresses that teachers address the unique needs of each student in the classroom in a way that capitalizes on their strengths to meet educational goals. Best practices, such as those given above, and reasonable accommodations need to be made to promote access and achievement in mathematics for all students.

References:

Garrison, L & Mora, J. K. (1999). Adapting mathematics instruction for English language learners: The language-concept connection. In *National Council of Teachers of Mathematics. Changing the faces of mathematics: Perspectives on Latinos* (pp. 35-47). Reston VA: National Council of Teachers of Mathematics.

Gee, J. P. (1992). *The social mind, language, ideology, and social practice.* New York: Bergin & Garvey.

Gonzales, N., et al. (1995). Funds of knowledge for teaching in Latino households. *Urban Education*, 29(4) 443-470.

Khisty, L. L. & Viego, G. (1999). Challenging conventional wisdom: A case study. In *National Council of Teachers of Mathematics. Changing the faces of mathematics: Perspectives on Latinos* (pp. 35–47). Reston VA: National Council of Teachers of Mathematics.

Krashen, S. (1981). *Second language acquisition and second language learning.* London: Pergamon Press.

National Council of Teachers of Mathematics (NCTM). (2000). *Principles and standards for school mathematics.* Reston: VA: National Council of Teachers of Mathematics. 60.

Tikunoff, W. (1985). Applying significant bilingual instructional features in the classroom. Part C Bilingual Education Research Series. Rosslyn, VA: National Clearinghouse for Bilingual Education. (ERIC Document Reproduction Service No. ED 338 106).

Kathryn Heinze teaches in the Graduate School of Education at Hamline University in St. Paul, Minnesota. Since receiving an M.A. in ESL from the University of Minnesota, she has spent thirty years in the classroom as an ESL teacher and teacher educator. Recently, she has focused on helping teachers make mathematics instruction more accessible to ELs.

Professional Development

Data-Driven Decision Making

Using Assessment to Inform Instruction and Improve Student Achievement

As mathematics educators, we understand the importance of assessment to the mathematics teaching/learning process. Assessment is an important and essential tool for teachers to use to improve instruction. In fact, it is assessment that truly distinguishes between teaching and learning. But what is it that distinguishes effective assessment from routine, calendar-based assessment? How does a teacher ensure that assessment informs teaching in a meaningful way, one that consistently shapes students learning?

Put simply, it requires data-driven decision making based on an ongoing assessment cycle. Teachers need to take the data collected from their students' performance on various assessments and use this data to make decisions on next steps for instruction.

The Assessment Cycle

To be truly effective, assessment must be embedded in the teaching and learning process, not just administered out of context at set intervals during the school year. Ongoing assessment helps teachers fine-tune the teaching process to ensure student understanding of mathematical concepts. Assessment must gather a bounty of information in order to help teachers measure student progress and glean students' potential. To this end, teachers should strive to keep accurate and dated information on their

students' progress in mathematics throughout the learning process.

Consider the following three stages of the assessment cycle:

- **Stage 1:** Identify what is to be taught, how it will be taught, and how to assess student learning.
- **Stage 2:** Gather evidence of student learning, interpret student responses, and record data.
- **Stage 3:** Act on the results. How does the data impact my teaching methods? What concepts need to be retaught?

The implementation of these types of assessments across all grade levels will help guide instruction and also provide a road map that leads students to mastery of core curriculum content and skills.

Stages of the Assessment Cycle	
Stage 1	Do students possess crucial prerequisite skills and knowledge? Do students already know some of the material that is to be taught?
Stage 2	Are students progressing adequately toward achieving the standards?
Stage 3	Have students achieved the goals defined by a given standard of a group of standards?

Forms of Assessment

In order to effectively measure mathematical learning, teachers must make sure we include various forms of assessment. A complete assessment program should include multiple measures:

Diagnostic: The purpose of a diagnostic assessment is to determine whether the student has the skills and knowledge necessary to begin the chapter, or if the student needs intervention prior to beginning the chapter.

Formative: Daily formative assessment should include scaffolding questions as well as talking, thinking, and writing about mathematics.

Summative: Summative assessment helps the teacher determine whether the students have learned the material that they were taught throughout the chapter.

Assessment to Guide Instruction

Assessment allows the teacher to consider the strengths and challenges of students; the effectiveness of the mathematics curriculum; and the next steps that should be taken in the instructional process. Some ways to use assessment to guide instruction are:

- ✔ Pose a "Talk About It" question during a lesson. Encourage students to work in small groups, discussing possible solutions to the question.
- ✔ Probe for prior knowledge before the introduction of a new concept.
- ✔ Observe students while they are working either in groups or individually which will give you information regarding their understanding of mathematics.
- ✔ Conduct student interviews which will offer an opportunity to use questioning strategies to explore an individual student's understanding of a concept.

Assessment: A Complete System

Assessment comes in many forms: diagnostic, formative, and summative. True assessment is dynamic and rich with information concerning student potential and performance. Assessment is the contributing force in improving the teaching and learning of mathematics for all students.

It is the most effective way to distinguish between teaching and learning, both in the classroom and at the district or state level.

References

Long, Donna. *Using Test Results to Inform Instruction and Improve Student Achievement,* Eisenhower National Clearinghouse, January, 2003.

National Council of Teachers of Mathematics (NCTM). Mathematics Assessment: A Practical Handbook, Reston, VA, 2003.

Wahlstrom, Deborah. *Using DATA to Improve Student Achievement,* Successline Inc., 1999.

Professional Development

Diagnostic	Determine whether students have the skills and knowledge necessary to be successful in subsequent lessons.
Formative	Include various forms of daily assessment such as talking, thinking, and writing about mathematics.
Summative	Determine whether students have mastered the material they were taught.

Donna Long is currently the Elementary Mathematics Marketing Manager for Macmillan/ McGraw-Hill. She has served as the National Mathematics Consultant for Macmillan/McGraw-Hill, the National Mathematics Assessment Consultant for CTB/McGraw-Hill, and the Mathematics/Title I Coordinator, Grades K-12, for an urban school district in Indianapolis, Indiana. She has also served as the Mathematics Program Coordinator for Curriculum and Assessment at the Indiana Department of Education.

Professional Development

Intervention: Bridging the Gaps in Student Learning

It is rare to find an elementary classroom where all of the students are on the same level in mathematics. Often when standards change or students are not at the same level in mathematics, teachers feel the need to push through the mathematics curriculum, even if students are lacking prerequisite skills necessary to succeed. Teaching new mathematics standards to elementary students is analogous to teaching students to swim: expecting students to instantly rise to the rigor of new standards, without bridging the gaps between the old and new standards, sets students up for failure.

In the opinion of many experts in the field, many mathematics programs have provided "inadequate textbooks and inadequate instruction" (Wu, 1998). To avoid such mistakes again, a successful program must provide a systematic way for teachers to bridge the mathematical gaps of students who are accustomed to less rigorous standards. For these reasons, all mathematics programs need to supply teachers with effective tools they can use for assessment and instruction of prerequisite skills.

Entry-Level Assessment: Identifying the Gaps

To accurately inform teaching decisions in the classroom, entry-level, or diagnostic, assessment should be given to students before each chapter. Entry-level assessment should not test new content; it should only test for skills required to proceed successfully into the new content. Such a test helps teachers determine what prerequisite skills students do understand and what skills need to be strengthened before proceeding into the new content. Entry-level assessment should not merely be given and then set aside; the results of entry-level assessment should be used to guide instruction throughout a chapter.

After completing this diagnostic assessment, an effective mathematics program provides different types of intervention and support for different students: intensive, strategic, benchmark, and above-level.

Intensive Intervention

This level of intervention is for students who are two or more years behind grade-level in mathematics. They need intensive instruction provided in an environment outside of the normal classroom for at least 2 hours per day. Ideally, these skill building lessons will not merely be worksheets distributed to students for independent, repetitive practice. And, they should not be merely row after row of exercises.

Intensive intervention should be designed to reteach concepts and skills, thus improving every student's mathematical understanding and procedures. Skill building lessons that are visual and require minimal amounts of reading enable students to work on their own.

" Teaching new mathematics standards to elementary students is analogous to teaching students to swim: expecting students to instantly rise to the rigor of new standards, without bridging the gaps between the old and new standards, sets students up for failure."

Stepped out models and guided practice of strategies to help students bridge their skill gaps should be provided, before students practice independently. Manipulative activities and games are greatly useful in sustaining interest and engagement during this relearning stage. By following such a structure, students can learn the concepts, skills, and procedures they were lacking.

Strategic Intervention

Students at this level are struggling but still on grade-level. With sustained attention and guidance, a teacher can help lift a student back to the benchmark level without intensive intervention. McGraw-Hill's *Strategic Intervention Guide* provides a complete lesson plan, including goals, questions, and activities that complement the skill building page the students are using. Further, and most importantly, it provides follow up diagnosis and further intervention for students who, having completed the skill builder, still lack the mathematical skills they need to progress.

Benchmark and Above-Level Students

At the same time, students who do have the required prerequisite skills need to be appropriately challenged so they are continually improving their mathematical understanding and do not become bored. For students who do have the necessary prerequisite skills to continue onto new math concepts, skill building activities are not the answer. These on level and advanced students benefit from activities providing a variety of math challenges and experiences they can work on independently. Whenever possible, the teacher should strive to give these students dedicated time as well. Students should be asked higher order thinking questions about the concepts (horizontal) and be challenged with the next grade level's curriculum (vertical).

Summary

Because of the sequential nature of mathematics, when students have deficiencies in their understanding of previous areas of emphasis, it becomes extremely difficult for them to understand new topics that are based on those understandings. Teachers can use entry-level tests, especially when the standards expected of the students have become more rigorous, and then use the results to inform instruction. "It is important that teachers go beyond simply calculating a score to examine each child's response to each item" (Cathcart, 2000). Students and teachers need to work together to build skills that are lacking by reteaching necessary prerequisite skills. A solid mathematics program will provide entry-level tests and skill

building activities based on the test items to enable students to bridge the gaps so they can move forward successfully.

References

Cathcart, W. George, Yvonne M. Pothier, James H. Vance, and Nadine S. Bezuk. Learning Mathematics in Elementary and Middle Schools. Columbus: Ohio: Prentice Hall, 2000.

Selby, Alan M. "Mathematics from Primary School to College." Mathematics Curriculum Notes, Volume 1B, August 1997.

Van De Walle, John. Elementary and Middle School Mathematics: Teaching Developmentally. White Plains, NY: Addison Wesley Longman, Inc., 1997.

Wu, H. "The Mathematics Education Reform: What is it and why should you care?" www.math.berkeley.edu/~wu/, 1998.

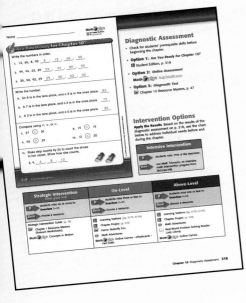

Robyn Silbey is a 30-plus year veteran of Montgomery County Public Schools in Maryland, currently working as a math content coach. She holds an M.S. in Elementary Mathematics Education from McDaniel College and a B.S. in Elementary Education from the University of Maryland. Robyn is a national consultant and serves as a teacher consultant in the Teaching Training Corps for the U.S. Department of Education.

Professional Development

What Does a CGI Classroom Look Like?
An Introduction to Cognitively Guided Instruction

Cognitively Guided Instruction, often abbreviated as CGI, is an approach to teaching mathematics that builds on children's natural problem-solving strategies. Based on over 20 years of research, CGI identifies specific strategies students use to help teachers understand how students think so that they can guide them toward mathematical understanding. So, you may ask, what does a CGI classroom actually look like?

Differences on the Surface

Pretend for a moment that you are observing three teachers all of whom are teaching the first-grade concept of subtraction using CGI. The first thing you would likely notice is that each has her or his classroom arranged differently. One teacher has students sitting at tables of four so that students can talk as they work. Another teacher has students sitting first on the carpet in a circle, and then allows them to spread out all over the room to work on problems individually in their math notebooks. The third teacher sits with a small group of students at a problem-solving center who share their strategies with each other. Obviously, using a CGI approach does not involve a particular class configuration.

In these classrooms, teachers pose different types of story problems to introduce subtraction. One teacher has addition and subtraction problems mixed together. Another teacher is using subtraction problems only, while the third teacher is using what appear to be missing-addend problems as well as more traditional subtraction problems. So, CGI does not use a pre-specified set of problems in a given sequence to teach the curriculum. Teachers who use CGI are not limited to specific resources, either. One teacher might read a children's book to provide context for the story problems. Another could refer to a recent field trip to a city park. A third might use a textbook as a teaching resource.

Similarities Underneath

Despite these differences, you would notice several important similarities. As we saw, all of these teachers use story problems to introduce a topic. Further, these teachers would not show the children how to solve these problems. In fact, teachers who use CGI usually tell the children to solve the problems any way they can. They also encourage students to use any tools they want, in a way that makes sense to them and that they can explain or show to another child, or to the teacher. When observing this for the first time, many teachers are mildly surprised that children have so much to say about math.

This may be surprising because so many of us rely on teacher's explanations and demonstrations to teach a concept or skill. This scenario reverses the usual order of instruction that many teachers follow. First, children solve problems and develop meaning for addition and subtraction.

" These teachers know that children are able to solve story problems without direct instruction on strategies, because children naturally direct model story situations about which they have informal knowledge. "

> *" Perhaps the most striking feature of CGI is that these teachers have a sense of ownership of this knowledge of children's thinking. It empowers them to make decisions, often on the spot."*

Then, they learn to write number sentences to represent addition and subtraction.

The Teacher's Role in CGI

CGI teacher use their knowledge of problem types and solution strategies to make decisions about their curriculum. This knowledge helps them determine what each child understands and then decide how to help the child extend their understanding. These teachers know that children are able to solve story problems without direct instruction on strategies, because children naturally direct model story situations about which they have informal knowledge.

For example, consider the following problem, called a "Separate Result Unknown" problem.
Jennifer has 17 pieces of candy. She gave 8 of the pieces of candy to her brother. How many pieces of candy does Jennifer have left?

Initially, most children use a tool such as cubes (or tallies or counters) to direct model this situation. They count out 17 cubes, remove 8 of them to show the candies that went to Jennifer's brother, and then count the number of cubes left. However, students may also apply more advanced strategies such as counting back from 17 to 8. They might even count up from 8 to 17 or derive 17 − 8 by figuring 17 − 7, which is 10, and then 10 − 1, which is 9.

CGI and the Benefit to Teachers

When you talk to the teachers about what they are going to do the next day, along with their mathematical goals, you hear them talking about the things they heard their students express and the strategies they saw their students use. They know what these strategies tell them about children's understanding of addition and subtraction.

Perhaps the most striking feature of CGI is that these teachers have a sense of ownership of this knowledge of children's thinking. It empowers them to make decisions, often on the spot. They know when to push, when to hold back, and how to make a problem easier or harder. They know how to support children to make sense of problems in their own ways. They know when to use a story problem and when not to. They know what problems to give next to support children's learning. They know how to listen. Most importantly, they say their curriculum is never quite the same from one year to the next, because the problems they pose depend on the children in their class.

Additional Reading:
Carpenter, T. P., Ansell, E., Franke, M. L., Fennema, E. & Weisbeck, L. (1993). Models of problem solving: A study of kindergarten children's problem-solving processes. *Journal for Research in Mathematics Education, 24*(5), 427-440.
Carpenter, T. P., Fennema, E., Franke, M., Levi, L. & Empson, S. B. (1999). *Children's Mathematics: Cognitively Guided Instruction.* Portsmouth, NH: Heinemann.
Carpenter, T. P., Fennema, E., Franke, M., Levi, L. & Empson, S. B. (2000). *Cognitively Guided Instruction: A Research-Based Teacher Professional Development Program for Elementary Mathematics.* Research Report 003. Madison, WI: National Center for Improving Student Learning and Achievement in Mathematics and Science.
Carpenter, T. P., Franke, M., & Levi, L. (2003). *Thinking mathematically: Integrating Arithmetic and Algebra in Elementary School.* Portsmouth, NH: Heinemann.

Susan B. Empson is an Associate Professor of Science and Mathematics Education at The University of Texas at Austin. She earned her Ph.D. in Mathematics Education at the University of Wisconsin-Madison and has worked on the Cognitively Guided Instruction project. Her research has been supported by the National Science Foundation and the Spencer Foundation, and published in such journals as *Cognition and Instruction, Journal for Research in Mathematics Education, Teaching Children Mathematics,* and *Journal of Mathematics Teacher Education.*

Professional Development

Professional Development

Literature and Math: Making the Connection

The level of excitement was palpable in every classroom, corridor, and office of the elementary school I was visiting for an assembly program about my mathematical children's books. Inspired by *How Much Is a Million?*, the students decided to surprise me with a collection of one million popcorn kernels. However, they did far more than simply gather heaps of corn. They predicted, they estimated, they calculated. They kept track of their progress through graphs and tables. They raised mathematical questions, solved mathematical problems, and thought mathematically.

Young children answered questions like, "If we each bring in 10 popcorn kernels, how many will we contribute?" Older students wrote out five and six digit numbers, discussing place value. Teachers asked "How many more do we need before we have a million?" Older students solved problems like, "If

we keep collecting corn at this rate, how long will it take to reach a million?" or "If 1,000 kernels fill this container, how large of a container will we need to hold a million?"

Now, after weeks of collecting corn and discussing the mathematics involved, everyone would get to see one million kernels today! The final 100 kernels were counted in unison by everyone in the school led by the principal over the PA system: "…999,997…999,998…999,999 …1,000,000!!!" The building rocked with cheers.

Making the Connection

Is it possible to get this level of excitement in your classroom, or even your entire school, all from the inspiration of a children's book? Certainly! *How Much Is a Million?* is a simple book that gets readers to visualize the magnitude of the numbers one million, one billion, and one trillion. It is written for young children, but it has been used by teachers of grades ranging from preschool through high school. The possibilities for using it are as vast as the numbers themselves.

How Much Is a Million? is certainly not the only book that has been used by teachers to help teach mathematics. Children's books are finding their way into the math classroom as teachers see the benefits of augmenting their mathematical teaching through literature. "To me, literature has always been

the key to kids' learning," says veteran teacher and Presidential Award Winner Kathy Reed. "From a very young age, children love books but they don't necessarily come to school with a love of mathematics. Through literature, I can take the inherent love kids have for books and tie it to math. A good book can bring the math lesson I'm teaching right into their world."

"Mathematics is a natural communication system that we can use to describe our world and communicate our experiences," according to David J. Whitin and Sandra Wilde (Whitin and Wilde, 2000). By sharing mathematical literature with students, teachers can foster not only vocabulary development but also the expression and comprehension of thoughts in mathematical terms. Discussion of the mathematical ideas in books can help teachers assess students' prior knowledge and address misconceptions.

Where to Begin?

The first task for a teacher interested in using literature in the math classroom is to select the book most appropriate for the task. One place to start is in McGraw-Hill's Math Connects. You will find optional literature connections for each lesson, all supported by teaching strategies and activities that connect to the lesson concept.

Teachers who want to choose their own literature should consider several criteria. Select books that:

✔ Both children and teachers will enjoy. A good book for mathematical literature is a good book—period.

✔ Inspire children's natural curiosity, ignite their imaginations, and encourage them to ask questions or respond in varied ways. By contrast, avoid didactic books that merely dress up a math lesson with pictures and/or a contrived storyline.

✔ Present the mathematics soundly and with visual representations that are accurate and inviting. Watch out for books in which the author employs math gimmicks.

✔ Have strong cross-curricular connections to science, social studies, art, music, and other areas of the curriculum. Through these books, students will come to appreciate the broad reach of mathematics.

Tips for Using Literature with Math

• Read the book aloud, cover to cover, for your own enjoyment. Return to it in a second reading to pull the math out of it.
• Look for just one math lesson at a time even if a book has many. You can always revisit it at another time to help with additional math concepts.
• Be open to student questions and comments—they may lead to an appropriate math lesson.
• Prepare by assembling manipulatives appropriate to the story you plan to read.

A Final Lesson

After reading *If You Made a Million,* a teacher told me she asked her students to explore one statement from the book. Working together, two students decided to refute my assertion that a million dollars in quarters would weigh as much as a whale. In a multi-step process involving multiplication and division, the students showed that a 60-ton blue whale would weigh as much as two and a half million dollars worth of quarters. They then wrote to tell me about my "mistake."

To me, it was not important whether I erred or they had misinterpreted my words. More importantly, the book had piqued their curiosity, inspired them to develop a mathematical strategy to solve a complex problem, and honed their basic math skills along the way. What more could a teacher hope for?

" Through literature, I can take the inherent love kids have for books and tie it to math. A good book can bring the math lesson I'm teaching right into their world."

Presidental Award
Winner Kathy Reed

References:
Schwartz, David M.. *If You Made a Million*. HarperTrophy, 1994.
Schwartz, David M.. *If You Hopped Like a Frog*. Scholastic Press, 1999.
Schwartz, David M.. *How Much is a Million*. HarperTrophy, 2005.
Whitin, David J. and Wilde, Sandra. *Read Any Good Math Lately? Children's Books for Mathematical Learning, K-6*. Heinemann, 1992. 6.

David M. Schwartz is the author of many children's books that make math come alive as well as a popular speaker for both children and educators. His books include *How Much is a Million?, If You Made a Million, G is for Googol,* and *If You Hopped Like a Frog.* You can learn more about David at www.davidschwartz.com.

Selected Research Bibliography

General Resources

Bransford, J. D., A. L. Brown, R. R. Cocking, et al. *How People Learn: Brain, Mind, Experience, and School.* Washington, DC: National Academy Press, 2000. 24.

Geary, D. C. *Children's Mathematical Development: Research and Practical Applications.* Washington, DC: American Psychological Association, 1994.

Grouws, Douglas A. ed. *Handbook of Research on Mathematics Teaching.* New York: Maxwell Macmillan, 1992.

Kloosterman, P. and P. H. Gainey. "Students' Thinking: Middle Grades Mathematics." *Research Ideas for the Classroom: Middle Grades Mathematics.* Reston: National Council of Teachers of Mathematics, 1993. 10.

National Research Council. *Helping Children Learn Mathematics.* Eds. J. Kilpatrick and J. Swafford, Mathematics Learning Study Committee, Center for Education, Division of Behavioral and Social Science and Education. Washington, DC: National Academy Press, 2002.

National Research Council. *How Students Learn: History, Mathematics, and Science in the Classroom.* Eds. M. S. Donovan and J. D. Bransford. Washington, DC: National Academy Press, 2002.

National Research Council. *Adding It Up: Helping Children Learn Mathematics.* Eds. J. Kilpatrick, J. Swafford, and B. Findell. Washington: National Academy Press, 2001.

Reys, Robert E., Mary M. Lindquist, Diana V. Lambdin, Marilyn N. Suydam, Nancy L. Smith. *Helping Children Learn Mathematics.* 7th Edition. TK: Wiley, 2003.

Selby, Alan M. "Mathematics from Primary School to College." *Mathematics Curriculum Notes* 1B (Aug 1997).

Siegler, R. S. *Children's Thinking.* 3rd Ed. Upper Saddle River: Prentice Hall, 1998.

Sutton, J. and A. Krueger, eds. *EDThoughts: What We Know About Mathematics Teaching and Learning.* Aurora: Mid-continent Research for Education and Learning, 2002.

Van de Walle, John A. *Elementary and Middle School Mathematics:* Teaching Developmentally. 3rd Ed. New York: Longman, 1998.

Assessment

Black, Paul and William Dylan. "Inside the Black Box: Raising Standards through Classroom Assessment." *Phi Delta Kappan* (Oct 1998): 139–148.

Newmann, F. M., A. S. Bryk, and J. K. Nagoka. *Authentic Intellectual Work and Standardized Tests: Conflict or Coexistence?* Chicago: Consortium on Chicago School Research, 2001.

Wilson, Linda and Patricia Ann Kenney. "Assessment." Eds. Jeremy Kilpatrick, W. Gary Martin, and Deborah Schifter. *A Research Companion to NCTM's Standards.* Reston: National Council of Teachers of Mathematics, forthcoming.

Differentiated Instruction

Alexander, P. A. "Training Analogical Reasoning Skills in the Gifted." *Roeper Review* 6:4 (1984): 191–193.

Banks, J. A. *Cultural Diversity and Education: Foundations, Curriculum and Teaching.* 4th Ed. *Multiethnic Education: Theory and Practice.* Boston: Allyn and Bacon, 2001.

Baroody, Arthur J. "An Investigative Approach to the Mathematics Instruction of Children Classified as Learning Disabled." Eds. D. Kim Reid, Wayne P. Hresko, and H. Lee Swanson. *Cognitive Approaches to Learning Disabilities.* Austin: Pro-Ed, 1996. 547–615.

Bley, Nancy and Carol Thornton. *Teaching Mathematics to the Learning Disabled.* 2nd Ed. Austin: Pro-Ed, 1989.

Brimijoin, K. E. Marquisee, and C. Tomlinson. "Using Data to Differentiate Instruction." *Educational Leadership* 60:5 (Feb 2003): 70–72.

"Strategies for Individualizing Instruction in Regular Classrooms." *Roeper Review* 17 (Sept 1994): 43–45.

Tomlinson, C. "The Mobius Effect: Addressing Learner Variance in Schools." *Journal of Learning Disabilities* 37:6 (2004): 516–524.

Tomlinson, C. "Quality Curriculum and Instruction for Highly Able Students." *Theory into Practice* 44:2 (2005): 160–166.

Tomlinson, C. "Reconcilable Differences: Standards-based Teaching and Differentiation." *Educational Leadership* 58:1 (Sept 2000): 6–11.

Tomlinson, C. A. *How to Differentiate Instruction in Mixed-ability Classroom.* 2nd Ed. Alexandria: Association for Supervision and Curriculum Development, 2001.

Tomlinson, C., C. Brighton, H. Hertberg, C. Callahan, T. Moon, K. Brimijoin, L. Conover, and T. Reynolds. "Differentiating Instruction in Response to Student Readiness, Interest, and Learning Profile in Academically Diverse Classrooms: A Review of Literature." *Journal for the Education of the Gifted* 27:2/3 (2004): 119–145.

Tomlinson, C. and L. Kalbfleisch. "Teach Me, Teach My Brain: A Call for Differentiated Classrooms." *Educational Leadership* (Nov 1998): 52–55.

English-Language Learners

Mohan, B. The Second Language as a Medium of Learning. Eds. B. Mohan, C. Leung, and C. Davison. *English as a Second Language in the Mainstream.* Harlow, UK: Longman, 2001. 107–126.

Nagy, W. "On the Role of Context in First- and Second-language Vocabulary Learning." Eds. N. Schmitt and M. McCarthy. *Vocabulary: Description, Acquisition, and Pedagogy.* Cambridge, UK: Cambridge University Press, 1997. 64–83.

Snow, M. A., M. Met, and F. Genesee. "A Conceptual Framework for the Integration of Language and Content in Second/Foreign Language Instruction." *TESOL Quarterly* 23:2 (1989): 201–217.

Swain, M. "Integrating Language and Content in Immersion Classrooms: Research Perspectives." *The Canadian Modern Language Review* 52:4 (1996): 529–548.

Foldables™/Graphic Organizers

Alvermann, D. E. and P. R. Boothby. "Children's Transfer of Graphic Organizer Instruction." *Reading Psychology* 7:2 (1986): 87–100.

Darch, C. B., D. W. Carnine, and E. J. Kameenui. "The Role of Graphic Organizers and Social Structure in Content Area Instruction." *Journal of Reading Behavior* 18:4 (1986): 275–295.

Mayer, R. E. "Can Advance Organizers Influence Meaningful Learning?" *Review of Educational Research* 49 (1979): 371–383.

Mayer, R. E. "Models of Understanding." *Review of Educational Research* 59:1 (1989): 43–64.

McLaughlin, E. M. "Effects of Graphic Organizers and Levels of Text Difficulty on Less-Proficient Fifth-Grade Reader's Comprehension of Expository Text." *Dissertation Abstracts International* 51:9A (Mar 1991): 3028.

Robinson, D. H. and D. A. Kiewra. "Visual Argument: Graphic Organizers are Superior to Outlines in Improving Learning from Text." *Journal of Educational Psychology* 87:3 (1996): 455–467.

Instructional Strategies

Balka, D. and R. Callan. *Math, Literature, and Manipulatives (4–6).* Rowley: Didax, 2001.

Buehl, D. *Classroom Strategies for Interactive Learning.* 2nd Ed. Newark: International Reading Association, 2001.

Carpenter, T. P. and R. Lehrer. "Teaching and Learning Mathematics with Understanding. Eds. E. Fennema and T. A. Romberg. *Mathematics Classrooms that Promote Understanding.* Mahwah, NJ, Lawrence Erlbaum, 1999. 19–32.

Carpenter, T. P., E. Fennema, M. L. Franke, L. Levi, and S. E. Empson. *Children's Mathematics: Cognitively Guided Instruction.* Westport: Heinemann, 1999.

Crawford, M. and M. Witte. "Strategies for Mathematics: Teaching in Context." *Educational Leadership* 57 (Nov 1999). ASCD.

Johnson, David W. and Rogert T. "An Overview of Cooperative Learning." Eds. J. Thousand, A. Villa and A. Nevin. *Creativity and Collaborative Learning.* Baltimore: Brookes Press, 1994.

Marzano, Robert J. "Building Background Knowledge for Academic Achievement: Research on What Works in Schools." 2004.

Newall, A. and P. S. Rosenbloom. "Mechanisms of Skill Acquisition and the Law of Practice." Ed. J. R. Anderson. *Cognitive Skills and Their Acquisition.* Hillsdale: Erlbaum, 1981.

Newby, T. J., P. A. Ertmer, and D. A. Stepich. "Instructional Analogies and the Learning of Concepts." *Educational Technology Research and Development* 43:1 (1995): 5–18.

Ripoll, T. "Why This Made Me Think of That." *Thinking and Reasoning* 4:1 (1999): 15–43.

Rosenshine, B. and C. C. Meister. "Reciprocal Teaching: A Review of the Research." *Review of Educational Research* 64:4 (1994): 479–530.

Rosenshine, B., C. Meister, and S. Chapman. "Teaching Students to Generate Questions: A Review of the Intervention Studies." *Review of Educational Research* 66:2 (1996): 181–221.

Ross, B. H. "This is Like That: The Use of Earlier Problems and the Separation of Similarity Effects." *Journal of Experimental Psychology* 13:4 (1987): 629–639.

Sowell, E. J. "Effects of Manipulative Materials in Mathematics Instruction." *Journal for Research in Mathematics Education* 20:5 (1989): 498–505.

Sparrow, L. and P. Swan. *Learning Math with Calculators: Activities for Grades 3–8.* Sausalito: Math Solutions Publications, 2001.

Trafton, P. R. "Toward More Effective, Efficient Instruction in Mathematics." *Elementary School Journal* 84:5 (1984): 514–528.

Mathematical Content

Anghileri, J. and D. C. Johnson. "Arithmetic Operations on Whole Numbers: Multiplication and Division." *Teaching Mathematics in Grades K–8.* Boston: Allyn and Bacon, 1992. 157–200.

Balka, Don S. and Richard J. Callan. *Math, Literature and Unifix: Making the Connection (3–6).* Rowley: Didax, 2001.

Behr, M. J. and T. R. Post. "Teaching Rational Number and Decimal Concepts." *Teaching Mathematics in Grades K–8: Research Based Methods.* Boston: Allyn and Bacon, 1992.

Bresser, R. and C. Holtzman. *Developing Number Sense-Grades 3–6.* TK: Math Solutions Publications, 1999.

Chapin, Suzanne, Alice Koziol, Jennifer MacPherson, and Carol Rezba. *Navigating through Data Analysis and Probability in Grades 3–5.* NCTM, 2003.

Clements, D. *Learning and Teaching Measurement.* Ralston: NCTM, 2003.

Edwards, Edgar L., Jr., ed. *Algebra for Everyone.* Ralston: NCTM, 1990.

Selected Research Bibliography

English, L. D. "Children's Reasoning in Classifying and Solving Computational Word Problems. Ed. L. D. English. *Mathematical Reasoning: Analogies, Metaphors and Images.* Mahwah: Lawrence Erlbaum, 1997. 191–220.

Franco, B., et al. *Understanding Geometry.* TK: Great Source Education Group, 1998.

Hoffer, A. R. and S. A. K. Hoffer. "Ratios and Proportional Thinking." *Teaching Mathematics in Grades K–8: Research Based Methods.* Boston: Allyn and Bacon, 1992.

Isaacs, A. C. and W. M. Carroll. "Strategies for Basic-Facts Instruction." *Teaching Children Mathematics* 5:9 (1999): 508–515.

Kaput, J. and J. E. Sims-Knight. "Errors in Translations to Algebraic Equations: Roots and Implications." *Focus on Learning Problems in Mathematics* 5:3 (1983): 63–78.

Lamon, S. *Teaching Fractions and Ratios for Understanding.* Mahwah: Lawrence Erlbaum Associates, 1999.

Rathmell, Edward C. "Using Thinking Strategies to Teach the Basic Facts." Ed. Marilyn N. Suydam. *Developing Computational Skills.* Reston: NCTM, 1978.

Saxe, G. B., M. Gearhart, and M. Seltzer. "Relations between Classroom Practices and Student Learning in the Domain of Fractions." *Cognition and Instruction* 17:1 (1999): 1–24.

Thornton, Carol A. and Paula J. Smith. "Action Research: Strategies for Learning Subtraction Facts." *Arithmetic Teacher* 35 (Apr 1988).

Trafton, P. and D. Thiesen. *Learning through Problems: Number Sense and Computational Strategies: A Resource for Teachers.* TK: Heinemann, 1999.

Trafton, P. R. and J. S. Zawojewski. "Meaning of Operations." *Arithmetic Teacher* 38 (1990).

Wu, H. "Basic Skills Versus Conceptual Understanding: A Bogus Dichotomy in Mathematics Education." *American Educator* (Fall 1999).

Problem Solving

Charles, R. I. and F. K. Lester, Jr. "An Evaluation of a Process Oriented Mathematical Problem-Solving Instructional Program in Grades 5 and 7." *Journal for Research in Mathematics Education* 15:1 (1984): 15–34.

Chen, Z. "Children's Analogical Problem Solving: The Effects of Superficial, Structural, and Procedural Similarities." *Journal of Experimental Child Psychology* 62:3 (1996): 410–431.

Gick, M. L. and K. J. Holyoak. "Analogical Problem Solving." *Cognitive Psychology* 12 (1980): 306–355.

Hiebert, J. "Signposts for Teaching Mathematics through Problem Solving." Eds. F. K. Lester, Jr. and R. I. Charles. *Teaching Mathematics through Problem Solving.* Reston: National Council of Teachers of Mathematics, 2003. 53–61.

Schroeder, T. L. and F. K. Lester, Jr. "Developing Understanding in Mathematics via Problem Solving." *New Directions for Elementary School Mathematics.* Reston: National Council of Teachers of Mathematics, 1989.

Stanic, G. M. A. and J. Kilpatrick. "Historical Perspectives on Problem Solving in the Mathematics Curriculum." Eds. R. I. Charles and E. A. Silver. *The Teaching and Assessing of Mathematical Problem Solving.* Reston: National Council of Teacher of Mathematics, 1989. 1–22.

Suydam, M. N. "Untangling Clues from Research on Problem Solving." Eds. S. Krulik and R. E. Reys. *Problem Solving in School Mathematics: 1980 Yearbook.* Reston: National Council of Teachers of Mathematics, 1980. 43.

Reading and Writing

Burton, Leone and Candia Morgan. "Mathematicians Writing." *Journal for Research in Mathematics Education* 31:4 (2000).

Carr, E. and D. Ogle. "K-W-L Plus: A Strategy for Comprehension and Summarization." *Journal of Reading* 30 (1987): 626–631.

Eanet, M. and A. Manzo. "R.E.A.P.–A Strategy for Improving Reading/Writing Study Skills." *Journal for Reading* 19 (1976): 647–652.

Fielding, L. G. and P. D. Pearson. "Synthesis of Research: Reading Comprehension: What Works." *Educational Leadership* 51:5 (1994): 62–67.

McGinley, W. and P. Denner. "Story Impressions: A Prereading/Writing Activity." *Journal of Reading* 31 (1987): 248–253.

McKeown, M., I. Beck, G. Sinatra, and J. Loxterman. "The Contribution of Prior Knowledge and Coherent Text to Comprehension." *Reading Research Quarterly* 27 (1992): 79–93.

Nagy, W. and P. Herman. "Breadth and Depth of Vocabulary Knowledge: Implication for Acquisition and Instruction." Eds. M. McKeown and M. Curties. *The Nature of Vocabulary Acquisition.* Hillsdale: Erlbaum, 1987.

Vygotsky, L. *Thought and Language.* Cambridge: MIT Press, 1962.

Whitin, David J. and Phyllis E. Whitin. "The 'Write' Way to Mathematical Understanding." Ed. Lorna J. Morrow. *Teaching and Learning of Algorithms in School Mathematics.* Reston: National Council of Teachers of Mathematics, Inc., 1998. 161–169.

Research Bibliography

National ESL Standards

GOAL 1 To use English to communicate in social settings

Standard 1:

Students will use English to interact and participate in social situations

- **a.** give and ask for information that communicates ideas
- **b.** share needs, feelings and thoughts
- **c.** employ body language and interpret nonverbal cues in social environments
- **d.** use communication to meet personal needs
- **e.** participate in discussions
- **f.** negotiate events and complete transactions

Standard 2:

Students will employ spoken and written English to express personal ideas, and demonstrate their inclusion in the English speaking environment

- **a.** discuss, join in or investigate activities of interest
- **b.** convey social and cultural ethics, traditions and norms
- **c.** communicate wants, thoughts and emotions
- **d.** take part in popular customs or traditions

Standard 3:

Students will use learned techniques to improve their ability to communicate in English

- **a.** investigate their theories of language use and structure
- **b.** mimic native speakers and listen attentively to how others use English
- **c.** think of other ways of saying things
- **d.** take notice and focus on specific sections and parts of language
- **e.** ask for assistance and assess feedback from others
- **f.** evaluate nonverbal and verbal cues
- **g.** monitor and appraise personal language development
- **h.** seek clarification in the primary language
- **i.** discover language "chunks" and use them appropriately
- **j.** choose varying forms of media to deepen comprehension
- **k.** attempt to speak, read, write and understand English
- **l.** apply context to help clarify meaning and build understanding

GOAL 2 To use English to achieve academically in all content areas

Standard 1:

Students will learn new content through communicating by speaking, reading and writing English in the classroom

- **a.** respond to implicit and explicit oral and written directions
- **b.** ask for and give explanations
- **c.** be involved in class, group and pair discussions
- **d.** pose and respond to questions
- **e.** ask for help and information as necessary
- **f.** handle interactions and bargain to complete assignments
- **g.** clarify actions
- **h.** broaden and expand on other's views and language
- **i.** communicate likes, dislikes, and needs

Standard 2:

Students will use English to acquire, sort out, create, and present content information in spoken and written forms

- **a.** compare and contrast information
- **b.** convince, debate, confer, assess, and defend ideas
- **c.** listen to, speak, read, and write about content
- **d.** assimilate information from oral and written forms
- **e.** retell information and sequences
- **f.** select, connect, and make information clear
- **g.** analyze, evaluate, synthesize, and infer ideas from various sources of information
- **h.** react to the work of peers and others
- **i.** represent and interpret information visually
- **j.** hypothesize and predict outcomes
- **k.** explore, create and ask questions to clarify ideas, information and content
- **l.** comprehend and generate procedural and academic vocabulary as well as text features specific to content areas
- **m.** display understanding by using and responding to language and content in multiple situations

Standard 3:

Students will use appropriate learning strategies to construct and apply academic knowledge

- **a.** pay attention to specific content information or language
- **b.** employ essential reading comprehension skills such as skimming, scanning, previewing, and revising text
- **c.** build meaning through context
- **d.** record key information (in first or second language) informally by taking notes and using them to remember ideas and linguistic information
- **e.** employ strategies that help construct and extend the knowledge base by monitoring and evaluating understanding, self-correcting as necessary

f. find out about and use techniques and environments that foster learning (e.g., when, where, how to study)

g. anticipate how and when to use cognitive strategies and use them appropriately during a learning task

h. vigorously connect new information to background knowledge

i. self-assess success and comprehension after finishing an assignment or task

j. identify situational learning needs and seek help from others (i.e.: teachers, classmates, other school professionals, family and community members)

k. mimic native English speakers behaviorally and linguistically to further internalize language

l. identify when first language and background knowledge applies to the learning environment and use it to deepen understanding

GOAL 3 To use English in socially and culturally appropriate ways

Standard 1:

Students will use the appropriate language variety, tone, formality and genre for the audience, purpose, and setting

a. change the degree of formality for different audiences and settings

b. Know and use standard English, colloquial speech and dialects appropriately

c. Use different writing styles for diverse audiences, purposes, and settings

d. use and react to slang properly

e. use and react to idioms properly

f. use and react to humor properly

g. decide when it is fitting to speak in a language other than English

h. understand which subjects are suitable for various social and learning situations

Standard 2:

Students will use nonverbal communication that suits the audience, intent, and environment

a. deduce and react properly to nonverbal cues and body language

b. demonstrate acceptable manners and suitable nonverbal classroom behaviors

c. vary the use of tone, volume, stress, and intonation as the situation demands

d. become aware of and adapt behavior in reaction to nonverbal signals

Standard 3:

Students will use new learning strategies to broaden their intercultural and linguistic competence

a. see and copy others speaking and behavior patterns of others in specific situations or settings

b. attempt adaptive language variations in various situations

c. continuously investigate and refine information about appropriate language use and behavior

d. determine the level of appropriateness of language use in various environments

e. evaluate language choices by what is most appropriate for the social context

f. practice variations of language in multiple settings

g. decide when slang use is appropriate

Credits

Literature Credits

A TREE IN THE FOREST Reprinted with the permission of Simon & Schuster Books for Young Readers, an imprint of Simon & Schuster Children's Publishing Division from A TREE IN THE FOREST by Jan Thornhill. Copyright © 1991 Jan Thornhill.

ALEXANDER, WHO USED TO BE RICH LAST SUNDAY Reprinted with the permission of Atheneum Books for Young Readers, an imprint of Simon & Schuster Children's Publishing Division from ALEXANDER WHO USED TO BE RICH LAST SUNDAY by Judith Viorst, illustrated by Ray

BETCHA! © 1997 BY S.D. SCHINDLER Used by permission of HarperCollins Publishers.

Book cover of TIGER MATH: LEARNING TO GRAPH FROM A BABY TIGER by Ann Whitehead Nagda and Cindy Bickel. Cover photograph © 2000 by the Denver Zoological Foundation Inc. Cover reprinted by permission of Henry Holt and Company.

CIRCUS CAPS FOR SALE Copyright © 1967, 2002 by Esphyr Slobodkina Used by permission of HarperCollins Publishers.

COUNTING JENNIE by Helena Clare Pittman. Copyright © 1993 by Helena Clare Pittman. Reprinted with the permission of Carolrhoda Books, a division of Lerner Publishing Group, Inc. All rights reserved. No part of this excerpt may be used or reproduced in any

Cover from A REMAINDER OF ONE by Elinor J. Pinczes, illustrated by Bonnie MacKain. Jacket art © 1995 by Bonnie MacKain. Reprinted by permission of Houghton Mifflin Company. All rights reserved.

Cover from DO YOU WANNA BET? by Jean Cushman, illustrated by Martha Weston. Cover illustration copyright © 1991 by Martha Weston. Reprinted by permission of Clarion Books, an imprint of Houghton Mifflin Company. All rights reserved.

Cover from HOTTEST, COLDEST, HIGHEST, DEEPEST by Steve Jenkins. Jacket art © 1998 by Steve Jenkins. Reprinted by permission of Houghton Mifflin Company. All rights reserved.

Cover from MY FULL MOON IS SQUARE by Elinor J. Pinczes, illustrated by Randall Enos. Jacket art © 2002 by Randall Enos. Reprinted by permission of Houghton Mifflin Company. All rights reserved.

Cover from THE WARLORD'S BEADS by Virginia Pilegard © 2001 used by permission of the publisher Pelican Publishing Company, Inc.

Cover from THE WARLORD'S PUZZLE by Virginia Pilegard © 2000 used by permission of the publisher Pelican Publishing Company, Inc.

Cover of 17 KINGS AND 42 ELEPHANTS by Margaret Mahy, illustrated by Patricia MacCarthy used with permission by Penguin Group (USA) Inc. All rights reserved.

Cover of A PLACE FOR ZERO: A MATH ADVENTURE.Used with permission by Charlesbridge Publishing, Inc. All rights reserved.

Cover of BEANSTALK: THE MEASURE OF A GIANT.Used with permission by Charlesbridge Publishing, Inc. All rights reserved.

Cover of CUT DOWN TO SIZE AT HIGH NOON used with permission by Charlesbridge Publishing, Inc. All rights reserved.

Cover of HENRY HIKES TO FITCHBURG by D.B. Johnson. Jacket art © 2000 by D.B. Johnson. Reprinted by permission of Houghton Mifflin Company. All rights reserved.

Cover of MATH MINI-MYSTERIES by Sandra Markle. Used with permission Sandra Markle. All rights reserved.

Cover of MEASURING PENNY written and illustrated by Loreen Leedy. Copyright © 1998 by Loreen Leedy. Reprinted by permission of Henry Holt and Company, LLC

Cover of MEASURING UP by Sandra Markle. Used with permission Sandra Markle. All rights reserved.

Cover of ONCE UPON A DIME. Used with permission by Charlesbridge Publishing, Inc. All rights reserved.

Cover of PIZZA COUNTING. Used with permission by Charlesbridge Publishing, Inc. All rights reserved.

Cover of SIR CUMFERENCE AND SWORD IN THE CONE. Used with permission by Charlesbridge Publishing, Inc. All rights reserved.

Cover of SIR CUMFERENCE AND THE FIRST ROUND TABLE by Cindy Neuschwander © 1997. Used with permission by Charlesbridge Publishing, Inc. All rights reserved.

Cover of SIR CUMFERENCE AND THE ISLE OF IMMETER.Used with permission by Charlesbridge Publishing, Inc. All rights reserved.

Cover of SIR CUMFERENCE AND THE KNIGHT OF ANGLELAND.Used with permission by Charlesbridge Publishing, Inc. All rights reserved.

Cover of SOLD! A MATHEMATICS TALE. Used with permission by Charlesbridge Publishing, Inc. All rights reserved.

Cover of TELLING TIME WITH BIG MAMA CAT by Dan Harper used with permission by Harcourt Brace & Company. All rights reserved.

Cover of TEN TIMES BETTER by Richard Michaelson published by permission of Marshall Cavendish Children's Books Copyright © 2000 All rights Reserved.

Cover of THE HUNDRED PENNY BOX by Sharon Bell Mathis used with permission by Penguin Group (USA) Inc. All rights reserved.

Cover of THE LIBRARIAN WHO MEASURED THE EARTH by Kathryn Lasky. Used with permission by Little Brown & Company. All rights reserved.

Cover of THE MITTEN adapted & illustrated by Jan Brett. Used by permission of Penguin Group USA, Inc. All rights reserved.

Cover of TWO OF EVERYTHING by Lily Toy Hong. Copyright © 1993 by Lily Toy Hong. Cover reprinted by permission of Albert Whitman & Company. All rights reserved.

Cover of ZACHARY ZORMER SHAPE TRANSFORMER. Used with permission by Charlesbridge Publishing, Inc. All rights reserved.

COYOTES ALL AROUND by Stuart J. Murphy. Illustrations Copyright © 2003 by Steve Bjorkman. Mathstart ™ is a Trademark of Harper Collins Publishers, Inc. Used by permission of Harper Collins Publishers.

DIVIDE AND RIDE. Illustrations copyright © 1997 by George Ulrich. Mathstart ™ is a Trademark of HarperCollins Publishers, Inc. Used by permission of HarperCollins Publishers.

FRACTION ACTION.Copyright © 1994 by Loreen Leedy. Reprinted by permission of Holiday House.

FRACTION FUN. Copyright © 1996 by Nancy Tobin. Reprinted by permission of Holiday House.

From FRACTIONS AND DECIMALS by Lucille Caron and Philip M. St. Jacques, copyright © 2000 by Lucille Caron and Philip M. St. Jacques. Published by Enslow Publishers, Inc., Berkley Heights, NJ. All rights reserved.

From PEZZETTINO by Leo Lionni, copyright © 1975 by Leo Lionni, renewed 2003 by Nora Lionni and Louis Mannie Lionni. Used by permission of Alfred A. Knopf, an imprint of Random House Children's Books, a division of Random House, Inc.

From SEA SQUARES by Joy Hulme. Text copyright © 1991 by Joy Hulme. Illustrations copyright © 1991 by Carol Schwartz. Reprinted by permission of Hyperion Books for Children. All rights reserved.

From THE FLY ON THE CEILING by Julie Glass and Richard Walz, copyright © 1998 by Julie Glass. Illustrations copyright © 1998 by Richard Walz. Used by permission of Random House Children's Books, a division of Random House, Inc.

GEOMETRY copyright © 2001 by Lucille Caron and Philip M. St. Jacques. Published by Enslow Publishers, Inc. Berkeley Heights, NJ. All Rights Reserved

GIVE ME HALF! Illustrations copyright © 2000 by G. Brian Karas. Mathstart ™ is a Trademark of HarperCollins Publishers, Inc. Used by permission of HarperCollins Publishers.

HOW DO YOU KNOW WHAT TIME IT IS? By Robert E. Wells. Copyright © 2002 by Robert E. Wells. Cover reprinted by permission of Albert Whitman & Company. All rights reserved.

HOW MUCH IS A MILLION? By David Schwartz Illustrations Copyright © 1993 by Steven Kellogg. Used by permission of HarperCollins Publishers.

HOW TALL, HOW SHORT, HOW FAR AWAY. Copyright © 1999 by Nancy Tobin. All rights reserved. Reprinted by permission of Holiday House, Inc.

IF YOU MADE A MILLION by David M. Schwartz. Illustrations copyright © 1989 by Steven Kellogg. Used by permission of Harper Collins Publishers.

Illustration by Debbie Tilley from SPAGHETTI AND MEATBALLS FOR ALL! by Marilyn Burns. A Marilyn Burns Brainy Day Book published by Scholastic Press. Copyright © 1997 by Marilyn burns Education Associates. Reprinted by permission.

Illustration by Harry Briggs from MATH FOR ALL SEASONS by Greg Tang. Scholastic Inc. Scholastic Press, Jacket art copyright © 2002 by Scholastic Inc. Reprinted by permission.

Illustration by Harry Briggs from THE BEST OF TIMES by Greg Tang. Scholastic Inc./Scholastic Press. Jacket art copyright © 2002 by Scholastic Inc. Reprinted by permission.

Illustration by Liza Woodruff from AMANDA BEAN'S AMAZING DREAM by Cindy Neuswander. A Marilyn Burns Brainy Day Book published by Scholastic Press. Copyright © 1998 by Marilyn Education Associates. Reprinted by permission of Scholastic Inc.

Illustration copyright © 1990 by Bruce Degen from THE MAGIC SCHOOL BUS LOST IN THE SOLAR SYSTEM by Joanne Cole. Reprinted by permission of Scholastic Inc. The Magic School Bus is a registered trademark of Scholastic Inc.

Illustration copyright © 1995 by James Warhola from IF YOU HOPPED LIKE A FROG by David Schwartz. Reprinted by permission of Scholastic Inc.

Illustration copyright © 2001 by Timothy Bush from MATH MAN by Teri Daniels. Scholastic Inc./ Orchard Books. Reprinted by permission of Scholastic Inc.

Jacket art copyright © 2001 by Linda S. Wingerter from ONE RIDDLE, ONE ANSWER by Lauren Thompson. Scholastic Inc. Scholastic Press. Reprinted by permission.

Jacket cover by Dena Schtzer, copyright © 1992 by Dena Schutzer., from A MILLION FISH...MORE OR LESS by Patricia Mc Kissack. Used by permission of Alfred A. Knopf, an imprint of Random House Children's Books, a division of Random House, Inc.

Jacket cover by James Ransome, copyright © 1993 by James Ransome, from SWEET CLARA AND THE FREEDOM QUILT by Deborah Hopkinson illustrated by James Ransome. Used by permission of Alfred A. Knopf, an imprint of Random House Children's Books, a division of

Jacket cover from 8000 STONES: A CHINESE FOLKTALE by Diane Wolkstein. Used by permission of Doubleday, a division of Random House, Inc.

LITTLE NUMBERS. by Edward Packard and illustrated by Salvatore Murdocca. Copyright © 2001 by Salvatore Murdocca. Reprinted with the permission of Millbrook Press, a division of Lerner Publishing Group, Inc. All rights reserved. No part of this excerpt may

MINNIE'S DINER: A MULTIPLYING MENU. Text copyright © 2004 Dayle Ann Dodds. Illustrations copyright © John Manders. Reproduced by permission of Candlewick Press, Cambridge, MA.

PIGS WILL BE PIGS. Reprinted with the permission of Simon & Schuster Books for Young Readers, an imprint of Simon & Schuster Children's Publishi

Reprinted with permission from G IS FOR GOOGOL by David Schwartz. Copyright © 1998 by David Schwartz, Illustrations copyright © 1998 by Marissa Moss. Tricycle Press, Berkeley, CA. www.tenspeed.com

Reprinted with the permission of Simon & Schuster Adult Publishing Group, from ODDS AND CHANCES FOR KIDS by Manfred G. Riedel. Copyright © 1979 by Manfred G. Riedel. All rights reserved.

Reprinted with the permission of Simon & Schuster Books for Young Readers, an imprint of Simon & Schuster Children's Publishing Division from SEWING QUILTS by Ann Turner, illustrated by Thomas B. Allen. Illustrations copyright © 1994 Thomas B. Allen.

ROOSTER'S OFF TO SEE THE WORLD. Reprinted with the permission of Simon & Schuster Books for Young Readers, an imprint of Simon & Schuster Children's Publishing Division by Eric Carle. Copyright © 1972 Eric Carle.

ROUND TRIP. Illustrations © 1983 by Ann Jonas. Used by permission of HarperCollins Publishers.

SHAPE UP! FUN WITH TRIANGLES AND OTHER POLYGONS. Copyright © 1998 by Nancy Tobin. Reprinted by permission of Holiday House.

SQUARE TRIANGLE ROUND SKINNY. Copyright © 2002 by Vladimir Radunsky. Reproduced by permission of Candlewick Press, Cambridge, MA.

THE MISSING PIECE MEETS THE BIG O © 1976 BY EVIL EYE MUSIC, INC. Used by permission of HarperCollins Publishers.

THE QUILT BLOCK HISTORY OF THE PIONEER DAYS by Mary Cobb. Illustrated by Jan Davey Ellis. Text copyright © 1995 by Mary Cobb. Illustrations copyright © 1995 by Jan Davey Ellis. Reprinted with the permission of Millbrook Press, a division of Lerner Publish

TOO MANY KANGAROO THINGS TO DO by Stuart Murphy , Art Copyright © 1996 by Kevin O'Malley. Used by permission of Harper Collins Publishers

TRH Photo Credits

TR1 George Diebold Photography/Getty Images; **TR22** Getty Images; **TR23** Ariel Skelley/Blend Images/CORBIS; **TR66** Ed-Imaging; **TR67** Doug Martin; **TR68** Bill Aron/Photo Edit; **TR69** Doug Martin; **TR70** Ed-Imaging; **TR71** Macmillan McGraw-Hill Companies; **TR72** Ed-Imaging; **TR73** Doug Martin; **TR74** Richard Hutchings/Digital Light Source; **TR75** Doug Martin; **TR76** Ed-Imaging; **TR77** Macmillan McGraw-Hill Companies; **TR78** (t) Eclipse Studios, (b) Macmillan McGraw-Hill Companies; **TR79** Macmillan McGraw-Hill Companies